The
Happy Farmers

we
the story of a partnership

by
Sheila Wenham

Logaston Press
1989

LOGASTON PRESS
Little Logaston Woonton Almeley
Herefordshire HR3 6QH

First published by Logaston Press 1989
Copyright © Sheila Wenham 1989

ISBN 0 9510242 4 8

Photoset in Baskerville 10/13 pt by Logaston Press
and printed in Great Britain on Five Seasons 100 per cent
recycled paper by Ebenezer Baylis & Son, Worcester

To
Mary, with love

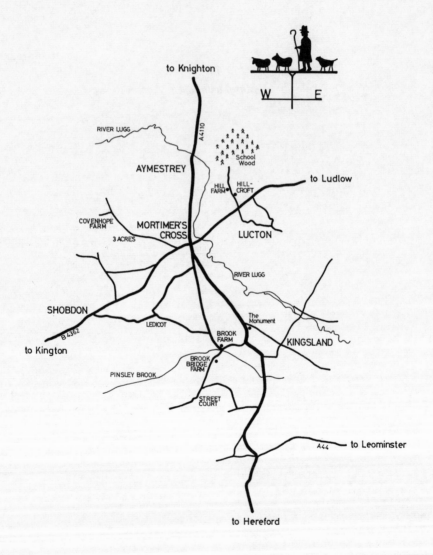

to Knighton

W   E

RIVER LUGG

A4110

School Wood

AYMESTREY

to Ludlow

HILL FARM • • HILL-CROFT

COVENHOPE FARM

MORTIMER'S CROSS

LUCTON

3 ACRES

RIVER LUGG

SHOBDON

The Monument

LEDICOT

BROOK FARM

B 4362

KINGSLAND

to Kington

BROOK BRIDGE FARM •

PINSLEY BROOK

STREET COURT

A44   to Leominster

to Hereford

Contents

PART I: Brook Farm, Kingsland: 1947–1970

1	Beginnings	1
2	Ways and Means	15
3	Brook Bridge	27
4	Kerry Hill Sheep	37
5	Showing—The Setting	53
	Showing—The Slog	64
6	Hereford Cattle	75
7	Retrenchment	83
8	Our Trip to America	93
9	Smallholders	131
10	The Dairy Herd	141
11	Interim	155

PART II: Hill Farm, Lucton: 1970–

12	'Retirement'	167
13	Hill Croft	175
14	Water	189
15	Ferny Patch	195
16	Welsh Mountain Ponies	199
17	Time for Thought	215
18	Winding Down	221
19	The Happy Farmers	231

Acknowledgements

I give my great gratitude to all who have helped me with our book: to John Cupper and John Hencher, who started me off when we thought it was too late and set my target; to my niece and nephew, Emma and Babar Khan Mumtaz, who patiently processed my scripts over three years of their incredibly busy life; to Chungaiz Khan and Aruna, who chose the title; to Pamela Jones, who coped with the photocopies; to Kate Ashley, who helped with the maps and to Steve Wolstencroft, who drew them; to Terry Court, who swiftly supplied some dates and figures; to the kind friends who read my scripts and encouraged me with comments and criticism; to the Farmer and Stock Breeder for several excellent photographs; to my publishers, Andy Johnson and Steve Punter, who helped me so patiently to make this a book of which we can all be proud; and above everything to Mary, without whom it could not have been written.

Sheila Wenham
October 1989

A Foreword

Three years or so ago I received an article from Sheila; she had recorded in the fifties a trip that she and Mary had made to the USA. I was intrigued; it described in vivid detail their experiences—the places they had seen, the people met, the land and the animals, the minutiae of the holiday, like witnessing self-service for the first time and visiting a baseball game. I realised that many others would enjoy reading this piece in the same way—but I wanted more. I felt that Sheila should tell the whole story. I wanted to know how a school teacher had become a farmer, how a close friendship had been forged more than forty years ago, and also how two women had succeeded in the male dominated farming world.

Of course I knew that Sheila and Mary were not ordinary; they did not fit into conventional patterns. I met them about twelve years ago when I was a sort of 'middleman' in their generous offering of Hill Croft; several friends and acquaintances came to stay there. It provided a haven for many an over-stressed city-dweller; all the visitors to Hill Croft left refreshed and grateful. Since then we have met from time to time, exchanged newsful letters and telephone calls, and learned much about each other.

I always look forward to a visit to Hill Farm. Sheila and Mary are interested in everything and everyone; they always want to know where I have been, whom I had met, the books I have read, the theatres I have visited. They usually have a list of topics we must discuss, and a selection of newspaper cuttings to be taken away. Over the years I have been amazed at the energy they put into their lives: their work is structured carefully and the same amount of thoroughness has been put into their 'causes'.

Into this structure Sheila had managed to fit her writing time—and I have looked forward enormously to the chapters of 'The Happy Farmers' that have arrived through my letterbox over the months. About a year ago a deadline was fixed; Sheila would try to complete the text by Easter 1989. I write this a few weeks before Easter, and everything seems to be going to plan (I never doubted that the book would be finished on time!) In spite of Mary's ill-health over the last few months, and the consequent reorganising of the Hill Farm schedules, Sheila has kept on writing.

The story of 'The Happy Farmers' is a fascinating one. I feel enormously privileged to have played one very small part in it. My life has been much enriched by knowing Sheila and Mary, and I know that many who read their story will be inspired by it. It is a moving account of a long friendship and business partnership; it is a story of achievement, but more than that, it tells us what can be achieved by true commitment, true devotion and true harmony.

John Cupper
February 1989

I
Beginnings

We met at a Hereford bull sale in 1944. I was there to watch the trade, hoping to re-start my small pedigree herd. I saw a vacant ringside seat beside a nice-looking girl in Land Army uniform, with small boy in tow. I joined them, gave young Aubrey a chocolate biscuit, and between bulls we talked.

Mary was working as stockman for Frank Roberts of Bromley Court, Hoarwithy. Their bulls had been through the ring and she and Aubrey had come round to see the rest of the sale. I don't remember the trade, being much more interested in Mary.

Our next meeting was over a year later. Kind neighbours of mine at Brook Farm thought that I should hit it off with the new landgirl working for their niece's husband, Bob Bywater, of Pedwardine. They invited us both to tea, we recognised each other immediately, and hit it off indeed we did!

Mary left school in 1938. At Cheltenham she shone with her 'cello, and she planned to take up her place at the Royal College of Music in 1939. Meanwhile she and her mother set off by sea for a long visit to their relatives in New Zealand, after a time of tension until Neville Chamberlain and Hitler signed the Munich Agreement. Mary and her mother achieved their holiday, but soon after their return war was declared, and Mrs. Elliott decreed: 'No London for Mary'. After some odd farming jobs locally, and with Uncle Harold Thomason's polo ponies in Leicestershire, Mary joined the Land Army and the beloved 'cello was laid aside for future generations. It is now with great-nephew Tom Beach at Shrewsbury School.

After training at Seale Hayne, and a dud job 'with horses'—one old Shire, two house cows, and an old man, a retired Eton master—(she stayed a month!), Mary joined the Roberts at Bromley Court. There followed three happy years, during which two of the six Roberts children were born; everyone worked flat out except on Sundays (when stock only were seen to), and Mary felt one of the family. She left sadly, in 1945, to be with her mother at their lovely old home, the Bridge House, Leintwardine. Her elder sister Ruth, also in the Land Army, had taken a living-in job near Leominster, so Mary sought somewhere within bicycling distance of Leintwardine. She worked at Pedwardine for eighteen months. In those days acres of roots were hoed by hand, with a line of men and girls stretched across the field, straight at work's beginning, serrated by the end of the day. There was much chat and leg-pulling—Mary gained a lot of earthy experience at Pedwardine.

She left in 1946 to join her mother and Ruth farm hunting. Their plan was to buy a place in Herefordshire which the sisters could farm in partnership, with Mrs. Elliott reigning in house and garden. They looked at many, aiming at between one and two hundred acres, but always the land was too rough or too dear, the buildings in disrepair, or the house faced the wrong way. (It's always a great mistake to try to buy a farm on the house.) Eventually they found a possible place, and I didn't realise at the time what a close shave I had when they were underbidders on The Rhyse, near Lyonshall.

During this late summer and autumn of 1946, between farm looking and a holiday with her mother, Mary came often to Kingsland to help me with the work. We were painting on the roof of one of the cow pens at Brook Farm when I experienced one of those rare moments of intuition, and knew that I could not do without Mary in my life.

I started farming in 1935. I had left college at Dartford in 1929 and was living happily at Maltman's Green (M.G.), Gerrard's Cross, teaching P.T., supervising the children's farm, and enjoying the company of some splendid people, many of whom have remained life long friends. When my father, a chartered accountant, offered me the farmhouse and a few acres of land that he was adding to his establishment at Armscote, near Stratford-on-Avon, I turned it down. I seldom went home in the holidays after my mother died (when I was sixteen), as I didn't get on with my stepmother; but I was curious to see the 'beautiful old Cotswold stone farm house with rucks of outbuildings' (actually a very nice stable yard) which Dad had just bought, so I spent a week or two there one holiday. There was heaps to do on the farm, and I was working alone on some poultry wire when I felt my roots go down a bit, and knew that this could be a place for me. A year or two later Dad was able to buy the long coveted Mansil's, right opposite his Ladle Farm. He offered me the charming little stone house, with yard, small buildings and an orchard, and after a lot of thought I accepted. I wasn't sure how I should manage financially—I had a very small income apart from my M.G. salary, but farming was in deep depression, and with room only for a few pigs and poultry, I didn't see how I could make a go of it. However, I had been at M.G. for over five years, could never face another school after that, and knew that my future lay in farming. I took the plunge.

At first I was desperately homesick for M.G., though many people came to me at weekends and holidays to help me with the work; but I made friends in the village, enjoyed the freedom from timetable, and had good support from our dear nannie and helper, Ethel Price, who left us when Mother died to marry Bob, a smallholder in Kingsland, Herefordshire. I wrote to her frequently—they both took the greatest interest in my farming doings.

I started with just two sows; but it had been arranged that for a small wage I should run the family poultry, which gave me a bit more room. My stepmother wanted a flock of Indian Game—beautiful table birds and 'very picturesque'—so a clutch of eggs was bought and I went ahead from there, hatching under broody hens and running the flock free range on Ladle Farm. Once, I left the broodies off their nests all day while I was at the Three Counties Show. Much

Sheila's Morris Minor, with Bob and Ethel, 1929

shaken, I drove them in at night, they resumed their own places, and the eggs hatched well—a lucky escape, never to be chanced again.

After a year or so my father offered me his twenty little crossbred ewes at twenty seven and sixpence apiece—they might have made thirty bob in market. They had been a nuisance breaking out, and needed more labour than was available. The plan was for me to take them over and run them round the farm free of charge. Dad bought many rolls of wire netting and my life with sheep began. Work was harder but I was still able to help exercise the horses on early winter mornings and enjoy my regular day a week with the Warwickshire in the golden time when George Gillson was hunting hounds.

On September 3rd 1939, war was declared. My father ordered the horses to be turned out and most of the farm to be ploughed up for corn. I was deeply anxious—there would be no grazing for my sheep, now increased in number and a pedigree flock. One day I was shattered to meet Allen Moy, my father's workman, coming round the corner with horse and cart, piled high with all the rolls of sheep wire pulled up from the hedges. I asked him where he was off to,

4

and he replied: 'The Master wants them stacked on the roadside, ready to roll across for a barrier if invaders come.' This decided me—I must find my own farm.

I was able to buy Buckley Green, Henley-in-Arden, in 1940. When I told Dad he remarked: 'Rather suburban, isn't it?' He was right, it was—and I hope still is—in the Birmingham green belt, a grass farm of eighty acres, to which I was able to add an adjoining ten. Most of the ground ran up a steep hill, crowned with horse chestnuts; but the twenty acres or so of bottom land was heavy clay, and had to be ploughed. A sympathetic War Ag. Inspector let me off lightly, but it was desperately hard work. The house was too large, but well built and very pleasant, standing in its own green, on a quiet lane, with a cottage set back out of sight. The whole cost £4,500.

When the war broke out the English Folk Dance Society was concluding its summer school at Stratford. Several of the staff had been staying with me at Armscote, and one of them, Catherine Huskisson remained, as friend and housekeeper, to help me with the move and to run the odd and ever-changing household at Buckley Green. 'Husky' was an ample, sweet-tempered lady whose sympathetic dancing and teaching enhanced the pleasure of the E.F.D.S. summer schools.

We started with a man in the cottage and a splendid young girl, Helen Kitchen, cousin of one of my M.G. friends. She stayed with me throughout—a tremendous worker and very strong. In the school holidays we had various helpers, several of them from Roedean— they hoed roots and pitched corn, and we all felt part of the 'war effort'; but it was fraught for me at times. A dray load of loose hay was turned over while I was milking, late at night in that horrible double summer time; and once, when I had to go to London to do a broadcast the girls forgot to put out the milk churns for collection.

My broadcasting was a small but lucrative sideline. I did several talks from Birmingham about women in war-time farming, 'digging for victory' and so on; but the London assignment was a much bigger affair, a trans-atlantic exchange between two women in war-time Britain and two in an America still at peace. The programme was something of an innovation and there were a few butterflies in the studio as well as in my tummy; but my partner was Nancy Spain, ex-Roedean and an experienced broadcaster, so we managed all right. Nancy was killed tragically in an air crash after the war.

I got home very late that night, and the forgotten churns of milk still in the dairy next morning did not help the work of the day. We hand milked ten or a dozen Shorthorn cows—a great help financially, but we had a bad go of contagious abortion, and the horror of finding a foetus lying in the gutter behind a poor tied-up cow is with me still.

Then came the bombing. The steep grassy embankment of a disused railway line ran right through the farm; great fun for lambs at play, but no doubt looking from the air like a rail approach to Birmingham. One night a raider dropped a string of bombs neatly on either side of the embankment, leaving a line of craters and one unexploded bomb, which was dealt with in the morning by firemen from Henley. One of our grazing sows was marooned on the far side of the embankment—it took ages to persuade her to come home across the line of fire.

On the night of the devastation of Coventry the cattle stampeded. We went out to see if we could calm them, and from the top of the hill we saw the city in flames. The next day a pall of gloom lay over the whole country.

Soon after this my workman left—a bomb had fallen just outside his garden, and it was hard on his sick wife. We had a year with no man on the place, and I was thankful to find John, a tall, strong and cheerful lad of nineteen, who walked up each day from Henley.

Husky too had left, after a row. The way I treated her remains one of my deep regrets in life.

There followed a series of unsatisfactory housekeepers, and I was getting very tired. Out of the blue one day came a letter from my father, in which he asked: 'Have you ever thought of selling Buckley Green?' I hadn't, but at once I knew that this was what I must do. I would go as paying guest to Ethel and Bob in Kingsland, where I would enjoy peace and quiet (with delicious meals brought to me on a tray!) while I looked for a farm in Herefordshire. It didn't quite work out that way, but I embarked.

I sold Buckley Green by myself the evening after the first small ad. in the Birmingham Post. I asked and received double my purchase price three years before. As always with a quick sale I thought I might have had more money; but it was a trouble-free transaction, very different from some of the goings-on these days. I was told afterwards that several farmers had failed at Buckley Green, (one of them by an extraordinary coincidence being a relative of Mary by marriage.) I do not feel that I failed, but my stay was not long enough to do the place justice—it was a challenging and very useful farm for me.

I sold all the stock except the two ponies, Polly and her daughter Beth, and the best of the sheep. These I parked in fives with friends all over the country, until I could gather them again in Herefordshire. My furniture went into store in Kingsland, and I landed myself, dog Hemp, and six-toed cat Meesch, at The Willows.

Sheila at The Willows, Kingsland c. 1928

7

Before I left Buckley Green I bought Brook Farm, an immaculate smallholding of twenty-five acres in a hamlet just a mile from Kingsland village. It belonged to two elderly sisters, who handmilked a small herd of beloved cows and were much worried by the ploughing-up orders. Their War Ag. inspector, a retired farmer and breeder of Kerry Hill sheep, whom we called Pa Pugh, was a neighbour of Bob and Ethel and knew my position. He thought that Brook Farm could be bought, and introduced me. I went down and spent some time with the old ladies, walking round the little fields of beautiful old turf—ten enclosures, the largest four acres, the smallest less than half, all fenced with tidy hand-trimmed hawthorn hedges. The house was tiny, with few mod. cons. There was a good old barn, once thatched no doubt, but now tin roofed, and a variety of shack-like buildings round a muddy yard. No water was laid on to the fields—there was a hand pump from the well at the back door, and the cows were driven night and morning to drink in the Pinsley Brook across the road. There would be a lot for me to do, but time was on my side; the sisters needed a rest, would talk it over, and let me know.

Weeks passed with no word and I became uneasy. One October afternoon the Kerry Hill Flock Competition judges had come from the Welsh Border to Warwickshire to place my flock. I made a sudden decision, requested a lift, picked up a toothbrush and was dropped in Kingsland just before milking time. I greeted Bob, who was hard at it, borrowed Ethel's bike, and reached Brook Farm in time to give the sisters a hand—they were running late after hard work in the cider orchard. Afterwards we talked, they decided that I was a proper person to follow them, and we agreed that I should buy the farm for £4,000, but that they should continue with house and orchard rent free for two years, while they found another home. We shook hands and I returned to the Willows for the night. I don't remember how I got back to Buckley Green.

Two days later the sisters telephoned to run back—they must have at least another thousand! I agreed swiftly, got my solicitor on to theirs, and the deal went through.

Brook Farm was a base—splendid for cattle, all right for ewes and lambs, but too small, too flat, and too good for young hill sheep. I looked at several places, but it was hard to find anything suitable, up out of the valley, yet close enough to run from the Brook. Then came incredible good fortune: I heard by telephone that a little hill farm up at Lucton might be for sale. The vendor, a Leominster merchant, had come by it only the year before, possibly in settlement of a debt; maybe it was another small farm which had failed to support its hardworking owner. He had planted up the old cider orchard, sunk a well, with windmill and reservoir, installed a man and family, and would I like to see it? He seemed very keen to sell, and I was doubtful. However, he offered to drive me the two miles from Brook Farm; we jolted together up the rough steep lane, and there it was— thirty-two acres of banky fields lying in the eye of the sun and the arms of the forest. There was a little old house, part black and white, part rough cast, some old buildings, and a modern three-bay Dutch barn which had been burnt down recently, and rebuilt, with its own tortured tin roof. Hill Farm had been part of the Croft Castle estate, sold off with many other holdings in the big dispersal of 1923.

When I looked a second time at the farm Arthur Duggan was digging in his garden. I asked him whether he would stay on if I bought, and work for me. He paused, foot on spade, and replied 'I don't mind if I do.' There began forty-two years with never a cross word between us. I bought Hill Farm in 1945 for £1,250.

When Mary started coming to help me, in the early autumn of 1946, I was nearing the end of two unhappy, lonely years. Biking to work from the Willows, and back for meals, had proved too difficult, and I was living in a caravan, parked on the far side of the Paddock at Brook Farm. The winters were rough, with a lot of wind, which wrenched open the door and blew out the oil lamp from time to time. Dog Hemp slept on my bed and was a great comfort. But the sisters had become disagreeable, resenting my presence at work around the buildings, which we shared—they had kept a house cow—and taunting me with ignorance when I lost a beautiful

Hereford heifer with yew poisoning—a neighbour had thrown his wilted clippings within her reach. She died in great pain.

At last came the appointed time and the sisters departed—poor things, no doubt they were devastated at leaving their beloved place. They had allowed me into the house to plan the alterations and additions, which were limited strictly by war-time regulations, still in force, and the builder, Arthur Deacon, got his men in as soon as the house was empty. We were able to lift the kitchen ceiling, build a bathroom and loo above, fit in a downstairs loo, and make an east window by my bed, and another in the sitting room, so that the telephone could be answered from outside.

Things were taking shape. Young Raymond Jones, who helped the sisters of an evening, had just left school, and I took him on full time. He lived across the Brook below Street Court, where his father was head groom. Raymond had one leg in irons, from early polio, and the courage of that small boy, in his disability and pain, mirrored the courage of the fine workman and cricketer who is such a help and comfort to us now.

Then, out of the blue one day, there cycled merrily up the drive a young girl and her mother. They jumped off their bikes on the yard and asked straight away whether Pamela could work for me. I was taken aback: I was still in the caravan, and had not considered what help I might want in the house. I hedged—'in a little while, perhaps—when had you thought of starting?' 'On Monday' was the reply—Pamela had finished with school on Friday! She could clean the caravan, and then each room of the house as the builders moved out. She could also cook my breakfast while I was round the farm (which she did, and had more than she bargained for when the oil stove went up in smoke, smothering my laid-out hunting clothes and everything else with black smuts.) Still demurring, I asked what made her think of coming to me for a job. 'Because you wave to the school bus' was the reply. I gave in, and so it all began.

There was little romance between the young boy, miserably operating the semi-rotary pump at the back door, and the young girl scrubbing floors inside—that was to come later. Meanwhile, in November 1946, I moved into the house.

I spent Christmas at Armscote with my family, while Mary drove from Leintwardine twice a day to help Raymond with the animals. This was the last time I saw my father; he died at the end of that cruel winter. I was grateful to Mary for making it possible for me to go.

Soon after my return I was invited to Mrs. Elliott's Christmas party at the Lion Hotel in Leintwardine. It was hot and crowded, and Mary developed a cracking headache, so we slipped back to the Bridge House and had a little time alone together in the empty house before I returned to the Lion, and reported to her mother that Mary was all right, but had gone to bed. Shortly after I took my leave and drove back to Brook Farm desolate.

On January 3rd 1947 the Radnor and West Hereford hounds met at Sarnesfield. We arranged to go. Mary had to drive to Leominster to pick up a young mare of Charlie Coxon's at Dishley Court, and I had to collect Bracken, whom I was riding for Colonel Cole, from The Croase in Kingsland. We would meet at Bainstree Cross. Mary was late: I waited, rode back towards Leominster to meet her, and then we trotted on together. Fortunately hounds moved off our way, and we joined them along the road. They soon found, so we had no time for talk, and there followed a busy day, with lots of jumping. I was not surprised that Mary was not there when hounds went home—the mare was young and green, and Mary would have eased her, and returned her early to Dishley. We would chat on the telephone in the evening.

I rode for home in the tired and happy mood which comes often after hunting, when you feel at one with your horse and the quiet winter countryside. Near Milton a car approached slowly, stopped well short of us, and Father Ward walked down the road: he was a Roman Catholic priest who often followed hounds by car. We met, and he said at once: 'Mary Elliott has had a serious accident—she's been taken to Leominster Cottage Hospital.' I have often regretted my discourtesy to the priest in exclaiming 'My God!' but it was a cry

11

from the heart and I would be forgiven. He told me briefly that Mary had been found, face down in liquid mud, in Sherington orchard — it looked as if the mare had gone one way round a tree and she the other. She must have been found soon, or she could have suffocated in the mud; but even the gentle rolling over must have been full of peril for her broken neck.

Father Ward held Bracken while I went into Milton to ring Mary's mother. Then I made for home as fast as I could ask Bracken to go after such a day. Somehow I got her to The Croase, did her up for the night, and was back at Brook Farm in time to be picked up, still in muddy hunting clothes, by Mrs. Elliott on her way to the hospital.

Mary was lying on her back, barely conscious, her face covered in blood. We spoke to her, and while her mother was talking to Matron I kissed her. Then there was nothing for us to do but wait.

After two or three days she was moved, still on her back, in to a single room, as the noise of the ward split her head. X-rays showed nothing, they said, but she must remain flat on her back for at least two weeks. I went in to see her each evening and with Matron's permission, was able to slip round the back and in at her French window. We talked a lot, and one night I asked her to join me in a farming partnership. Neither of us knew whether she would be able ever again to do manual work, but we knew that we must be together, and she accepted. We decided not to tell her family until she was home.

By the end of two weeks there was little improvement — it still pained her to lift her head, and she began to lose movement in her right hand. Her brother-in-law, Alan Beach, the Leintwardine G.P., wanted a second opinion, and it was decided that Mary should return to his house, to be nursed by her sister Margaret. Meanwhile an appointment was made with a Birmingham specialist.

The cruel winter of 1947 had set in: there was lying snow, intense frost, and the roads were awful. I offered to drive Mary and her mother into Birmingham in my good old 'Flying Standard' saloon, the best car I have ever owned. (Its number was CNX 598; it's

12

extraordinary how the memory holds over the years when now a name is forgotten within five minutes!) Mrs. Elliott accepted—with trepidation, I guess, but she did not show it. We set out, with Mary, propped by cushions, half reclining in the back. Despite a snail's crawl drive and many hair-raising skids we made it in time. I sat in the car off the Hagley road for what seemed ages. I was bitterly cold and desperately anxious. At last they came out, and almost without a word we drove off to find somewhere to drink our coffee. Near Halesowen I pulled off on to the edge of a piece of waste ground, where the snow was piled high, and children were tobogganing merrily.

Then I heard the verdict: the X-rays showed a dislocated cervical vertebra. An operation could be attempted, with a 50:50 chance of success. On the other hand, with patient rest, time might heal. It was Mary's choice. We all thought, and conferred, and when she decided 'NO op.' the relief was immense. From that moment, she began to improve.

On February 6th 1947 we told Mary's mother and her sister Ruth of our partnership plans. Mrs. Elliott was enthusiastic and congratulated us, but reproached Mary afterwards for letting Ruth give up her job in Scotland. Ruth was calm and quiet, and we did not know what she was thinking. Later, when we told Margaret and Alan, there was silence until Alan said 'Poor Ruth'.

The hard weather continued. When I visited Mary at the Bridge House after work I would often stay the night, slipping out in the early morning, with freezing nostrils, to drive back to join Raymond for milking and calf suckling. Many evenings were spent in family discussions over Mary's finance. Our partnership would be 50:50 throughout, except that for a time it would pay rent to me for Hill Farm—Mary bought her half share later on. She would realise her grandfather's small legacy, her mother would lend her some money free of interest, and Margaret promised a little at a very low rate. We were all set for our valuation and legal partnership agreement on March 25th. 'Better to tie you up for three years' said our local solicitor. Forty-two years on we remember that saying and smile.

March came, and with it lambing, and the end of my visits to Leintwardine. I was tied to the ewes night and day. The weather continued to be awful: lambs froze as they dropped—I tried to be there for every birth. My father had a stroke and died at Armscote, but I could not get there. Pamela became ill and I had to cope with house and food as well. It was a desperate time; but Mary made a quick decision and came to me, almost in a dressing gown! She could not do much outside, but the joy and relief for me to have her in the house, with food and comfort, and care for starving lambs, was immense. Our long life together had begun.

The winter blew itself out with a terrific gale on the night of March 23rd: Mary lay in bed afraid for me as I went round the stock in a tempest of whirling slates and falling branches; but we all survived, and on March 25th Geoffrey Chambers of Russell, Baldwin and Bright, came for our valuation. He stayed to lunch, and the Aga went out—it was one of the old sort, which need regular riddling, and was a devil to start again. Pamela, shaken by this, and excited by her first luncheon guest, dropped her dish of beautiful mashed potato upside down on the kitchen floor. She burst into tears, Geoffrey was sweet to her, and we all ate her delicious bread and butter with our meat and veg. We talk of it to this day.

The valuation of land and stock was completed, we signed our partnership agreement, Mary paid me cash for her half share, and as from March 25th 1947 we embarked on our long and happy haul.

II
Ways and Means

The small farm now had to carry two of us, and pay. I was not worried about this at first—war time prices were holding, and demand was good. Throughout, the sheep were our mainstay. The small herd of pedigree Hereford cattle was supplemented by the sale of stores, bought as calves in Hereford market, suckled on cross-bred cows at Lucton, and yarded there, to be sold as strong yearlings. At the Brook we kept two house cows, who also suckled many calves,

Brook Farm house, 1947

besides providing us with milk and butter, and the pigs with skim. (It was very hard work hauling strong calves off a full udder before milking out by hand!)

Then there were the cash crops: we grew some wheat at first on the rich land at Brook Farm, so reluctantly ploughed by the sisters, but laid this back to grass as soon as possible, and increased the sheep. The ground at Lucton was not strong enough for wheat; we grew oats and roots for our own consumption, and had a go at early potatoes. They could be money-spinners—we grew Arran Pilot, and have continued to do so in the garden ever since—but they were also one of our worst headaches. They needed planting in February, to catch the early market: there was always the anxiety that the ground would not be fit by then, though with the light Lucton land we were usually lucky. We planted by hand behind the horses; Arthur would draw a furrow with the ridging plough, turn on the 'adland', and split the ridges to cover, while we adjusted our speed to keep ahead. There would be three or four planters—ourselves, Raymond, and perhaps 'Old Ren', whom we collected from his home in Hereford Lane on our way up. He was a real old countryman, who helped us a lot.

Arthur with Lester and Dolly, c. 1948

16

Potato rising in June was a worry: the earlier in the month the better the price but the lighter the crop! 'New' potatoes had to be on the market the day after lifting, so timing was tricky, and the weather always a hazard. I hated wrestling with the merchant over price and plans. Then there were the pickers to hire: at first we tried boys from Lucton School, who were used to being sent out in teams on farm work during the war. We paid the school for their time, but much of our own was wasted fielding the potatoes they threw at each other, and urging them to fill the bags. These were hauled off the ground at the end of the day, weighed on the adland and re-loaded ready for the merchant's lorry in the evening—a lot of work for men and mares. We gave up the job when the price dropped heavily, and again laid more land down to grass.

Cider fruit has been our continuing, but very dodgy, cash crop. There was a mature orchard at Brook Farm, and I did not realise the gold mine that I gave the sisters when I let them have it for two years rent free. The fantastically high wartime prices held for several years, and Bulmers accepted all that was offered—genuine 'bitter-sweet' cider apples, perry pears, 'jam' apples, the lot. They supplied bags, and labour to unload at the factory; prisoners of war were on this job when first we went. Fruit could be taken without notice at any time on any day of the working week. Everyone jumped on the band wagon, from the large farmer to the man with one bitter-sweet tree in the garden: in the autumn of a good fruit year the busy approach roads to the city would be choked with mile long queues of lorries, trailers, tractors and cars, all waiting to turn into the factory gates. Once inside there was more waiting for a place at the channels, where bags must often be emptied upwards, on to an ever-rising mound of apples which the mill could not receive. Unloading help was a thing of the past, it was heavy work, and we never knew whether a journey to Bulmers would take two of us three hours or a whole day: work at home was hard to plan.

Then Bulmers increased their premises, reduced the price and issued delivery permits, and our guessing game began. Each year we

17

are invited to offer the number of tonnes we wish to sell. This must be estimated on the trees, and we used to pride ourselves on our accuracy—once the company congratulated us specially on this. Now there is a strong temptation to over-estimate, since the whole of the offer may not be accepted. The uncertainty, and the real price fall, have resulted in the grubbing up of hundreds of acres of old orchards, and probably the fruit from those that remain would be neither here nor there to Bulmers, with their own orchards in full production and their many specialist contract growers; but they have remained loyal to their small producers, and so have we to them. We have found the cider fruit a useful bonus crop, with grazing under the trees for most of the year; and we still enjoy the courtesy and welcome we receive from fruit office, weighbridge and channels. Now, in 1986, we have delivered in person to Bulmers for an unbroken thirty seven years. We hope to continue gently for a while yet.

When we started together at Brook Farm cash flow was a problem. There were three bank accounts, and when the farm received a major payment from the sale of stock or crops we would withdraw each into her own account, a 50:50 sum which we thought it could stand; but the farm could stand very little, having to provide weekly wages, stock feed, and other running expenses. I had a modest income after my relatives died, but Mary had nothing but the farm, plus £60 a year 'dress allowance' from her mother. She needed to service her small debt to Margaret, and to find her half share of the weekly housekeeping. I would subsidise her until the next farm payment came, but she felt she had nothing in hand for extras or presents, and her generous nature minded very much indeed. We cast around for ways to increase our weekly income: we started egg production, and tried small plots of flowers and vegetables for sale at the Womens' Institute stall in Leominster.

We were fortunate in having our books supervised and our accounts produced by Denis Dodd, a partner in my father's firm of chartered accountants. He kept an eagle eye on our affairs, demanding our books and every shred of evidence, including our day-to-day petty cash book, well before his annual visit from Birmingham. We analysed each enterprise in detail, so that we could drop quickly on any shortfall.

Denis's day with us was a gruelling session of questions, answers, and anxious searches for missing documents. We were exhausted by the end, but he taught us much and never charged a penny. We are so thankful to him. He has retired now, but we are in regular touch with a well-loved friend.

We worked fourteen hours a day or more, and were often tired and cross ('T and C'—and we had another 'check-row' phrase— 'Bootlaces', after Noel Coward.) Our rows were usually in the evening and seldom lasted overnight, though once Mary left the breakfast table and set off walking down Hereford Lane to leave me. At the Shobdon turn she remembered that Mrs. Donnelly was due to help Pamela with the spring cleaning. She was back in time to greet her.

Mary says that I was very hard on her mistakes: she would dissolve into tears when I harped on after an apology. One irritant to me was her frequent failure to secure the name, address, and telephone number of enquiring customers—they could be lost, and sometimes were! Another difficulty was her bad memory—we had to rely too much on mine, and I still find myself trying to do her thinking for her in quite an unnecessary way. I was not so patient with her shortcomings of youth as she is with mine of age.

The demands on her time by Mary's family were sometimes hard to bear. It amazes me that people who would not dream of calling a teacher from her class, or a doctor from his surgery, feel that a farmer can leave work easily. Relatives would descend upon us, to be fed and shown around, while Mrs. Elliott would arrange a holiday for herself and Mary, when the booking might fall in the middle of haymaking. We would have liked to get away together, but except for shows this was not possible in the summer.

There was little time for personal expenditure, and we lived sparingly, while the farm was almost self-supporting in stock feed. The oats which we grew at Lucton were cut by a contractor's binder and stooked in the field where, even in a good season, they must stay for over a fortnight to dry and ripen. In bad weather they must be opened up and re-stooked, perhaps again and again; a heart breaking job. A team of us would then haul with the mares—two vehicles going—to barn or rickyard, where the sheaves would be stacked for autumn threshing. This needed a team of five or six, to pitch on to the box, cut the string bands, feed into the insatiable machine, rake clear the straw and chaff which were spewed out in different places, and above all, to tend the bags, which filled with varying grades of corn in a steady stream—one hoped! Arthur carried the hundred-weight bags—we stopped him carrying two hundredweight, as was usual—up the granary steps and tipped the corn in loose piles onto the new floor, which divided laterally one bay of the Dutch barn. During the winter we collected from Lucton small loads of whole oats with pony and float, or car and trailer, and took them to the mill at Kingsland or Aymestrey for rolling. Some days later we picked up the crushed oats, and returned them to Lucton or the Brook, as needed. They were mixed daily with hay or straw chaff, chopped roots and mineral salts, to make a healthy, bulky feed on which cattle thrived; but labour was comparatively cheap in those days!

There was an access snag to Hill Farm: tall vehicles could not pass under the archway which spanned the long steep lane half way up from the Ludlow road. The threshing box had to ascend from the valley across neighbours' fields, for which wearisome journey permission could be withdrawn at any time. Stock lorries fared worse: they must reverse up the hill some three hundred yards, and drop the ramp at the archway to load. This meant that when we were selling cattle from Lucton we must drive the two miles up from the Brook before the lorry blocked the lane, and then keep watch between farm and archway to signal arrival, when we drove the cattle down to load. With a hired lorry this timing could be agony—the anxiety of being late for market is with me still!

Flock sign on the garage, Brook Farm

The beautiful stone archway carried the drive to Croft Castle from the South Lodge near Mortimer's Cross. Carriages would turn in through the wrought-iron gates, up the fine oak avenue, across the gated archway, and on up the south side of School Wood to the Castle. We have found traces of a building on our Hill Croft ground near the archway, surely the remains of another lodge, from which the keeper's wife would run to open the gates for the Croft carriage.

Modern needs are different: at some time during Arthur's tenancy of Hill Farm, when we went up too rarely, something mysterious happened to the archway—the road fell and was cleared—only the massive stone pillars remain. The Croft tenant of the Moors, also with access above the arch, was happy, and so was Arthur, and so, in the end, were we, for it would be impossible to farm as we do now with

21

such an obstacle. There was some talk by later Crofts of re-building, but this fell through—Lucton Lane is now the responsibility of the Council.

At about the same time as the archway disappeared, most of the magnificent oaks in the Moors avenue were felled without warning. These have now been replanted by the present owner of the Moors, Mrs. Croft-Murray. She has added a line of copper beech along the roadside, and a wood for the future on part of the land, earning the gratitude of many who look ahead.

Haymaking was another time consumer—it could drag on from June to August. We needed to finish at Brook Farm before starting at Lucton, because of the travelling for mares and implements. Arthur would drive down with Lester and Dolly hooked to the mowing machine, ride Lester back up, and come again in a day or two with the combined swathe turner and side-rake. We would turn and row-in

Haymaking

with Dolly, while one of us worked the corners with a pikle (pitch-fork). In catchy weather the swathes needed turning again and again — it was frustrating beyond belief to tool a horse round and round a field for hours, only to have rain descend again as one finished. If the swathes were turned too often with a machine the hay became 'wozzled up', and would not dry: then four or five of us would work it through with pikles, round and round the field for hours. We once put a rather senior pupil at this job, and after a long time I thought how bored she must be, and suggested that she knocked off, and did the routine egg collection which was due. She looked at me coldly, and said, 'I came here to learn hay-making'. I did the egg collection myself.

We hauled the hay loose, loading it with pikles on to dray and cart: each vehicle was fitted with 'thripples' ('raves' in Warwickshire) which extended the load fore and aft — in the cart the mare looked dwarfed beneath the load, which extended forward over her back. We worked a shuttle service to the buildings, and pikled the hay into the old barn, then on into the 'tollerts' (or lofts) above the cowpens. In winter it was fed down to the cattle, or carried in a 'sheet' (a split bag) to the sheep cratches out in the fields, sometimes with pony and float, more often on Mary's back.

We seldom made bad hay, and never had to buy any; once we even sold a rick! Labour was easy; good chaps were glad to come in the evening, and there was plenty of our special drink — cider and diluted lime juice, half and half. But it was a costly exercise for us. We ploughed our small profits back into the farm, and there was less and less money to come out. We tried to do more ourselves, but were always short of time, and Mary was despondent. We must alter things somehow.

I decided to give up hunting. I bought Bracken from Colonel Cole soon after Mary's accident, and had a couple of marvellous seasons on her, clipped and in top form; she was well known with the Radnor and West for her speed, stag-like jumping and spectacular buck! Mary had one day on Beth, but received such a raspberry from her sister Margaret, who declared her thoughtless and selfish, that she never hunted again. She became groom to Bracken on hunting days, and the warmth of her welcome home to us both was a great joy. But it could not go on: the time and energy of 'doing' a horse in the stable, and the daily exercise, got beyond us. There were young bulls to be prepared for the spring sales, and show sheep to be shorn and cared for. We tried a season with Bracken rough, and in the field all day, but this was not fair on her; so we put her and Beth in foal.

In those days the service of hunter mares was cheap and simple. Thoroughbred stallions, chosen and subsidised by the Hunter Improvement Society, travelled the counties, walking from farm to selected farm each day—the round journey took a week. The horse carried on his back his own and his groom's overnight luggage: the groom walked beside him, a stout hoof of ten miles or more each day. They stopped for lunch at a farm en route, where mares might be brought to meet them; and they might be visited in the evening at their night quarters. But if a mare's home lay on their route, as ours did, they would call in: it was a thrill for us to have a magnificent thoroughbred stallion clattering up the Brook Farm drive shouting to our mares in their boxes behind the house.

We bred from the mares for two years running. Bracken had a colt and a filly, both of whom we sold easily on her reputation as a good hunter: the filly, by Irish Dance—we named her Shamrock—was a beauty, and we heard later from the girl who bought her how well she was doing and how much she was loved. We were sorry to lose touch. Beth foaled first a rather plain grey filly called Jenny, whom we decided to keep a while; but her second foaling was a disaster: it was a breech presentation, we called the vet too late and the chestnut colt was dead when drawn.

We were hit hard by this happening and felt that we ought to stop dabbling in horse breeding and get on with the farming proper. Beth was nearly twenty, so we found a good home for her with a friend in Gloucestershire, where she lived happily with a donkey to a ripe old age. Bracken we lent to other friends who wanted a pleasant hack and would look after her; but soon after they had her a speeding motorbike came round the corner in a country lane and ran slap into her chest. Neither rider was badly hurt but Bracken's wind-pipe was severed and she died on the road—a sorry end for a grand little mare.

When she was weaned Jenny went as company for a foal of Veronica's at The Hill, Staunton. She stayed there for over a year and we had a foretaste of the future when she jumped out of her field to join some ridden horses on the drive, an enormous leap upwards over the guard wire and huge wide ditch of the Ha-ha. Her companion wisely did not follow.

When Jenny came back to us as a two year old we worked her in long reins and I backed her as I had backed her mother and grandmother before her: there was the same placid temperament and will to work, but a certain determination not to do things she disliked, such as crossing water. I had a lengthy battle with her over some flood water on a ride near Street Court and we were very late home for lunch—Mary was anxious, but I had to win. She was a nicely mannered pony when we advertised her for sale. A hunting farmer friend, David Powell, came to look at her for his grandson, John Williams of Harewood End: David thought Jenny was out of Bracken but he bought her all the same and she was a tremendous success. For years John jumped her at shows and Pony Club events all round the county—they collected a wealth of cups and rosettes; when John grew out of her his sister Fiona followed and Jenny flourished; but she never cared for water jumps!

In June 1968 Mary thought up a wonderful surprise for my sixtieth birthday: she borrowed Jenny for a week. John brought her to Brook Farm early in the morning—I never heard the horse box and when I went out to work at 7.30 as usual, there was Jenny grazing in the Paddock! It was a super surprise: we had some grand rides that week. We were re-discovering Lucton at the time and we rode up, one of us on a bike, and explored School Wood, which was magic for us then. (It has changed hands since and the new owner tries to refuse the rides to horses.) That borrowing of Jenny was a stroke of genius which I shall remember always.

Jenny was the last of our 'pleasure ponies': we knew in those early days that we had to make a go of our farming, so we decided to modernise and expand.

Sheila on Eaton Plunger at Brook Farm, 1950

III
Brook Bridge

The Brook is a small hamlet astride the Pinsley, a tributary of the River Lugg: four small houses lie, next to next, along the lane to the north, of which Brook Farm is the last, with its land stretching away north east towards Kingsland. We were soon able to add another eight acres to this, which took us to the Knighton–Hereford road, on the edge of Kingsland village. To the north west lay the Brook Meadows, ten acres which I had rented from Pa Pugh when I came first to Kingsland. In time, after a lot of persuasion, we were able to buy.

I used to drive Pa regularly to Kerry Hill council meetings in Shrewsbury and my persistence over the Brook meadows became almost a joke between us. He was a determined old gentleman, one of the 'fathers' of Kingsland Baptist Chapel, and the possession of land was for him a key factor in life. He gave way in the end and got his price and our gratitude: the Brook meadows were a useful addition to our growing farm.

Across the Brook, to the south, were five more houses: the lodge of the railway crossing keeper, who opened and closed the gates for the little old train which chugged once a day between Leominster and Kington; then three more cottages, belonging to Street Court, in one of which lived Raymond with his family; and finally Brook Bridge farmhouse and buildings, with over forty acres of good land, running down to the south bank of the Brook, and up the side of Street Court drive. The Roman road, Watling Street, cuts through

Brook Bridge Farm, 1967

the farm on its way from Shrewsbury to Hereford—we unearthed some huge paving slabs once, when setting a gate post.

I had walked Brook Bridge when I was looking for more land, before Mary joined me, and the elderly owner gave me 'first refusal'; but he was in no hurry to part, so I gave up hope, and bought Hill Farm. We never thought together of Brook Bridge until one day, when we were trimming sheep on the Brook Farm yard, running feet came up the drive and a breathless voice gasped 'Call the fire brigade—our barn is on fire!' We all ran with buckets, a chain from the Brook, but Kingsland brigade were there in five minutes; they saved the house and other buildings, but the Dutch barn, full of hay too quickly stacked, was burnt out. This knocked the stuffing out of our good neighbour, and soon afterwards he offered us the farm at a reasonable price, and we bought.

We now possessed well over a hundred acres of land, including a small, banky field up the Covernhope (pronounced Connop) valley, a mile south of Mortimer's Cross, which we rented early on, and

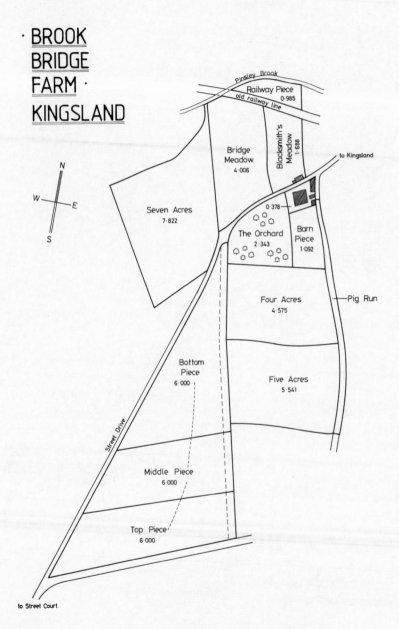

· BROOK
BRIDGE
FARM ·
KINGSLAND

N
W E
S

Pinsley Brook

Railway Piece
0·985
old railway line

Bridge
Meadow
4·006

Blacksmith's
Meadow
1·688

to Kingsland

Seven Acres
7·822

0·378

The Orchard
2·343

Barn
Piece
1·092

Four Acres
4·575

Pig Run

Bottom
Piece
6·000

Five Acres
5·541

Street Drive

Middle Piece
6·000

Top Piece
6·000

to Street Court

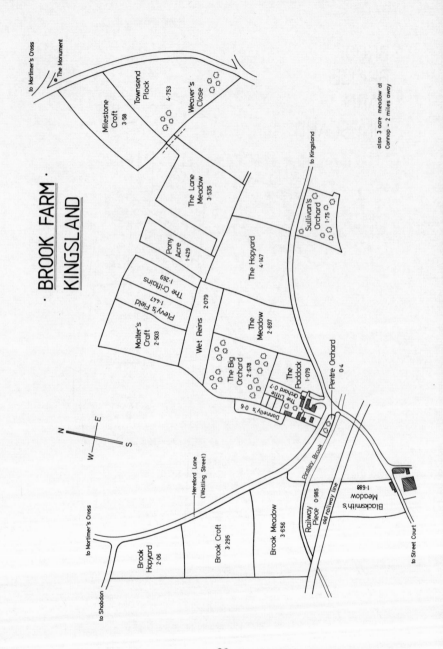

· BROOK FARM ·
KINGSLAND

to Mortimer's Cross

The Monument

Milestone Croft
3·58

Townsend Plock
4·753

Weaver's Close

The Lane Meadow
3·535

Pony Acre
1·429

The Crithains
1·269

Plevy's Field
1·447

Malter's Croft
2·503

Wet Reins
2·079

The Big Orchard
2·678

The Meadow
2·697

The Hopyard
4·147

Sullivan's Orchard
1·75

to Kingsland

The Little Orchard 0·7

Donnelly's 0·6

The Paddock
1·079

Pentre Orchard
0·4

Pinsley Brook

Hereford Lane (Watling Street)

to Mortimer's Cross

Brook Hopyard
2·06

Brook Croft
3·295

Brook Meadow
3·656

Railway Piece 0·985

old railway line

Blacksmith's Meadow
1·688

to Street Court

to Shobdon

N
W — E
S

also 3 acre meadow at Cannop – 2 miles away

later bought; and five small houses, because the two next door to Brook Farm became available, each with a bit of orchard, and we could not miss them! Nearly all my capital was swallowed, but the farming paid for a while, and Mary never faltered in her 50:50 contribution to the enterprise.

The Pentre, the house right next door, could not have come to us at a better time. Raymond had moved on to a man's job at Kingsland Saw Mills, and to our delight, in 1953, he and Pamela were married. I drove Pamela and her father to the wedding in Shobdon church and the happy couple back to the reception in the Village Hall. (It was good to have our large new Vauxhall Velox for this splendid occasion, but the car was too grand for us, and we soon changed it for a Morris Oxford van.) Raymond and Pamela lived for three years in a family house in Presteigne, with Pamela coming to work for us perched pillion on Raymond's motorbike; but when a death deprived them of their house, the Pentre was ready for them. They moved in next door to us, and on March 25th 1957, their elder daughter Sheila, our god-daughter, was born. It was lambing time: I was sleeping out in the buildings, and shall remember always the sound of Raymond's feet coming up the drive in the very early morning. We phoned for the midwife, and there followed a terribly anxious two days. In the end two doctors (the anaesthetist in evening dress) safely delivered that fine little girl.

Meanwhile Jim Davies and his family had come to Brook Bridge farmhouse. We were wonderfully lucky to have working for us two such skilled and complementary men as Arthur and Jim: Arthur, easy-going but with all the old farm crafts, steady and tireless all day behind the horses or expertly fencing and gate hanging; Jim the tractor man, careful and conscientious, a fine ploughman, tidy in all his work. Both were spare in build and quiet in character and they got on together famously. For us the joy of their tidy work, with another good boy from Kingsland School, Graham Edwards, to complete the team, made those some of the happiest years in our farming life.

31

We invested in a new Fordson Major tractor, a hydraulic plough, and hay making machinery. Jim would nip up to Lucton and do a day's ploughing for Arthur to work down and drill with the mares, while Arthur would come down on his bike for hoeing, harvesting, fencing and gate hanging. We set about Brook Bridge in some form: much worn out turf was ploughed up and a good corn—roots—ley rotation established. There were not many combines about yet: we still used a contractor's binder, and pitching the sheaves from a seven acre crop of magnificent wheat put paid to Mary's back for some time; she trimmed the sale sheep that year encased in plaster!

A deep wooded gully ran up the length of the farm: we mourned the boundary belt of beautiful oaks which were felled before we bought, but there was still plenty of coppice, bushes, and rough grass to make it an ideal run for pigs. We fenced it right round—a good thing that pig wire was cheap in those days—and set in a gate where the ground flattened into a paddock by the buildings. Here pig nuts could be fed, and water provided when the stream was dry. A large rough shelter of straw bales encased in sheep wire with a tin roof, completed our pig run, and we expanded into a small herd.

When I started at Brook Farm I reared a couple of bacon pigs in the excellent old-fashioned pigscot. One was sold, and the other shared with neighbours. The village butcher came on his bike and, attended by 'Old Ren' and Bob Price, hauled out my poor pig into the orchard, cut his throat with a knife, and strung him up by the hind legs to a tree for singeing. I can smell the fire now. He was cut up later, and Mrs. Ren came to salt down the bacon and make pies and puddings. These were good, but it was all a horrible business, never to be repeated.

Soon after Mary joined me we bought two ten-week-old Wessex Saddleback gilts (a gilt, or hilt, is a young female pig until she has weaned her first litter) from A.B. Williams' pedigree herd near Broadway. We drove them home, each enclosed in a roomy beet-pulp bag, in the back of the car. While they were growing we built on a second pigscot at Brook Farm, with brick walls and the same low roofed opening on to a separate concrete yard, with glazed drain-pipe halves built in as feed troughs. Between the two yards there was a double division, with a shuttered pop-hole to each cot, through which the little pigs could nip to and fro for creep feeding, or be shut away from the sow for handling or loading. Farrowing rails were fitted to the roomy interiors, and electricity for infra-red lamps wired in. It was a successful set-up for many years.

When those first pigs of the partnership, Eve and Lil, (the latter a relative of the devil!) were about ten months old we walked them a mile up the road to Frank Roberts' Large White boar at Ledicot. (By an extraordinary coincidence the Roberts had bought the neigh-bouring farm to Brook Bridge the year before Mary joined me.) The resulting pigs were the popular 'blue and whites', which we sold at eight weeks old in Hereford market, having cut the boars at six weeks. We did our own castrating (a retired farmer near Armscote

The sow Emma enjoying a good scratch

33

taught me) and never had a pig go wrong. Mary held them up by the hind legs, head between her knees, and when done lowered them back over the wall to a ranting mum, to whom they would run straight to suck. The squealing was the worst part of the whole thing.

Before they farrowed Eve and Lil ran out by day in the Little Orchard, with rings in their noses. (The pigs in the following Brook Bridge herd were not ringed, thank goodness—another horrible job we did ourselves.) We handled them a lot, and they would flop down to have their tummies rubbed, and would usually remain lying on their side until the massage ceased. This was a great advantage when farrowing, as so many piglets can be crushed by a restless sow. One of us tried always to be there during farrowing, rubbing and cosying till the sow settled, and then sitting on the farrowing rail in the infra-red light, watching as each piglet popped out perfect, and with hardly a pause, scrambled round mum's hind legs, fastened on to a teat, and sucked. Soon there would be a double row of little suckers, busy until they dropped off into serene sleep in the red glow of the lamp. The only other animal I know which produces at birth such active miniature adults is the guinea pig. I wonder whether this is the reason for the name in common?

Eve's first farrowing went fine, but Lil's was a disaster. I could not quieten her; she was hardly still for an instant, and in the end she attacked me. I vaulted out over the yard wall—no time to reach the door—but she ripped the seat out of my stout old hunting breeches as I went over the top. She then savaged the little pigs—only two of the nine or ten survived. We decided not to keep her, but several people who knew, advised us to try again. In trepidation we did so: she settled to farrow and we extracted each piglet, as it was born, into a box by the Aga. When we thought she had finished we tipped the whole box-full under the farrowing rail beside her udder, and left her to it. They sucked at once, she reared a beautiful litter, and we had no more trouble with her.

When the time came for the Brook Bridge herd, we reared four of the best of Eve's gilts, taking care that each had at least twelve well

34

placed drills; most important when you remember the double row of suckers! With Eve and Lil this gave us six sows, and we bought a Large White boar from old Mr. Coxon's well-known herd at Milton. We reckoned that this number of pigs was comfortable for our accommodation: as each sow came close to farrowing she was drawn from the Brook Bridge paddock, walked quietly down the road, over the bridge, and into one of the two Brook Farm farrowing pens. We had fenced in three sizeable runs, each with a hut, in the adjoining Little Orchard, so that when ready, or when the next sow needed a farrowing pen, the preceding litter could run out with mum until fit for sale. The system worked, (though we were lucky never to have three sows coming down within a few days of each other) and it was a happy herd, which paid. Of course its modest profit would not satisfy the present day intensive mania, but we would hate to be forced financially into keeping tethered sows, close-penned calves, or battery hens.

Recently we were shown an intensive pig herd: as we approached the buildings we heard a continuous rhythmic clanking, which we expected was some kind of food conveyor belt. Inside the dimly lit shed we found that the noise was made by the neck-chains of fifty or more tethered sows, standing in a long line of narrow stalls, and weaving their heads from side to side in an eternal search for food or freedom. They remained so, unable to turn, and with no bedding on the concrete floor, for the four months till farrowing, when they moved down a narrow passage into small individual pens, each with a creep rail and infra-red lamp for the piglets. Here they were tied again, still unable to turn, and gave birth and suckled until weaning time; then they walked round a corner to the boar, and when served returned to the line and so resumed the cycle. All the sows we saw looked well: we did not see the casualties, except for a boar who had 'gone off his legs'. The whole thing was a sickening experience of animal exploitation.

We were our own stockmen, and as numbers increased, so did our work. The men were on top of the field work, with no sprays used, and the farm looked good. We entered for a county competition for the best managed farm of between one hundred and a hundred and fifty acres, and we won the class. We received our award on the stage of the old Kemble theatre in Hereford, then the Corn Exchange, from the chairman of the Agricultural Committee, Mr. Percy Bradstock, much-respected veteran breeder of the Freetown herd of Hereford cattle. We were very proud.

All this was fine, but we were becoming overwhelmed. We did not want to increase the sheep beyond the number needed to produce twenty-five two year old ewes fit to win their class at the Craven Arms ewe sale each autumn. The various bunches of yearling ewes, older ewes, yearling rams and weaned lambs needed to be no bigger than we could handle in one session, for worming, foot-dressing and so on. We were busy trimming, and away regularly at shows. In the winter there were young bulls to be groomed and exercised, besides our regular routine of feeding, milking, shepherding and gardening. We must do something to lessen the load. The constant journeyings to and from Lucton were time consuming, and so was the planning there. We reckoned that with Brook Bridge now nearly all grass, and with the rough hill field at Connop as a change for the yearlings, we would have enough room without Lucton for the first class small flock of sheep we wanted.

After long and careful thought we offered the tenancy of Hill Farm to Arthur, and he jumped at it. He would come down and help us when we wanted him, paid on an hourly basis: we would have his rent, less wages to pay, and above all else, less work and worry. With hindsight, and with the tenancy law as it is, the risk we took of never regaining possession of this beautiful place was immense and frightening; but we never thought seriously then of living up here ourselves, with dicey water, no electricity, and the rough road. We concluded the Agreement with Arthur, and at Michaelmas 1953 he became our tenant. He remained so until 1970, when we regained possession.

IV
Kerry Hill Sheep

In March 1951, when I was chairman of the Kerry Hill Flock Book Society's Propaganda Committee, 'The Field' magazine printed an article of mine about Kerry Hill sheep in general and our flock in particular. I wrote: 'The Kerry Hill sheep is a native of the Kerry Hills, a grassy range running at a height of about 1,000 feet from Bishop's Castle, Shropshire to Newtown, Montgomeryshire. These hills have been famous as a sheep walk from time immemorial, but the first record that they carried a distinctive breed appeared in 1809 in the Agriculture Survey of Wales.

The breed probably had common origin with the Welsh Mountain sheep, became distinctive some long time before 1809, and received no outside blood until 1840, when it is recorded that the breeders from the Kerry Hills began to buy rams from Knighton, in Radnorshire. These rams, which were introduced systematically for fifteen years, seem to have been bred by crossing the speckle-faced Radnor ewes with the black-faced horned rams from the Long Mynd.

By 1855 a great change had taken place in the Kerry Hill sheep: the breeders had decided on the points they wanted...and had fixed the type. ...Ten years later breeders from both sides of the Welsh Border were buying rams from Kerry, and the foundations of the present day Kerry Hill sheep were firmly laid.

The closest attention had been paid to wool, a notable trait from the earliest records, and today a ewe will cut from 6 to 8lbs of fine quality wool which commands top market price. Conformation and meat-carrying quality were also improved, and maturity accelerated. The old hardiness was preserved, but the 'whitish' or tan face had given place to the sharply defined black and white markings of the modern sheep.

Indeed the modern Kerry Hill is a splendid sheep. The ewes are wonderful mothers—the alert, active appearance, the long head and roomy quarters are signs of the deep milking for which they are famous. Even with young ewes a flock average of one-and-a-half lambs is general, while with mature ewes one and three-quarters is often achieved.'

Commercial demand was great: farmers from all over the country came in the autumn to the Welsh Border sales to buy guaranteed young pure-bred ewes, Kerry Hill or Clun Forest, for crossing with Down rams for fat lamb production. Thousands of ewes, registered and unregistered, were penned each week at Craven Arms, Knighton, Kington, Kerry, and other centres, competing in their classes for the auctioneers' prizes for the best forty, thirty or twenty-five two year olds. It was a wonderful sight—each shepherd in the pen behind his ewes, alerting them to meet the buyers sharply, with every one of those hundreds of shining white Kerry faces washed with soap and water at home the day before.

The most exciting date for us was the Breed Society's Show and Sale at Kerry in early September. The long drive in the dawn was magic: through Leintwardine, past the great stock farms Stormer and Marlow, on up to Clun, over the narrow river bridge and into the hills, with the red rowan berries glinting by the roadside and the purple of the heather beginning to colour the slopes. Past the Anchor pub we went and topped Kerry Hill to meet the counties spread below, Montgomery, Merioneth and away to Cader Idris, with Kerry village tucked in beneath the hill. A cup of coffee on the top, then gently down to Glanmiheli, Mr. Ben Alderson's farm where the sale was held. The ewes were penned with hurdles in mid-field, but rams were our job at Kerry and we unloaded to join the long lines tied to low rails near the sale ring. The cream of the breed was there

Kerry Show and Sale, 1953. With Mr. J.C. Jones and our champion ram lamb

and the excitement was great when prices soared or a fresh young ram was placed above a Royal Show winner. After the sale customers sometimes asked us to load their purchases at Kerry station and we would lead a ram down the road to join his ewes and scramble with them into the waiting railway waggon for a long slow journey to the Midlands or South.

Some time during the day had come a brief word from kind Mr. Ben: 'See you at the house later on.' When the work was done we were thankful for the warm welcome from his three daughters to a table groaning with hams and pies, salads and trifles, scones and Welsh cakes: we were always tempted to stay too long enjoying the talk and laughter and the tales of a good buy or a record price. We drove home in twilight, tired but happy, full of affection for Glanmiheli and Mr. Ben Alderson. His famous flock, registered second in the Society's Book in 1900, was dispersed when he died, but his daughter Margaret Price retained a nucleus with the precious prefix 'Kerry' and is building up again. She won the small flock competition in 1986 and was elected President of the Society in 1988, a post held by her father in 1960: he would be proud of his daughter to-day.

Growing economic pressure on farming slowly changed the leisurely pace of shows and sales: few could afford a full time shepherd nor spare the time to be trimming ewes for days beforehand. The auctioneers could not afford the time spent judging the competition pens when they would have liked to be on with the selling. The pride in the tidy turnout was lost, and the sheep went untrimmed to the sales — most buyers would say none the worse for that, since the wool trimmed off was the rough which ran the rain off the fleece.

Meanwhile the trend towards cross-bred ewes for fat lamb production was growing. The Scottish Halfbred (Border Leicester ram on Cheviot ewe) was well established, and many Midland farmers went North instead of West for their replacements. Then some wise Welshmen formed the Welsh Halfbred Association, and launched, with splendid publicity, their Halfbred, a Welsh ewe with Border Leicester ram. Here the Kerry Hill Flock Book Society lost a golden opportunity: we should have promoted with vigour what we have always thought of as the original Welsh Halfbred, Kerry Hill ram on Welsh ewe. Instead, the Propaganda Committee voted no money at all for advertising! I should have resigned, but battled on — a losing struggle. The decline in commercial use of the pure bred Kerry as a crossing ewe was hastened by a developing fashion among breeders for an excessively short sharp head and ears, and a mass of black colour, which spilled over from nose to face, ears, and into the wool, spoiling it for dyeing into pastel shades for which Kerry Hill wool was valuable. The scale of the sheep was lost, and so was the milking capacity. Trade became poor, and many breeders dropped out: registered flocks dwindled to a handful, and in the 1980's the Flock Book Society considered applying for registration as a 'Rare Breed'. That point has not been reached: some stalwarts, with vision and large farms, have hung on to a few of their best sheep; new members are coming in from Ireland (always a centre of interest in the breed)

Flock Book Society annual dinner at the Elephant and Castle Hotel, Newtown, 1964

and from smallholders and schools with an interest in showing, some inspired, no doubt, by John Terry's amusing book 'Pigs in the Playground'. In 1986 the trade for Kerry Hill rams at Builth (sale centre now for the National Sheep Association) improved greatly: demonstrations of fat lambs by various rams showed the Kerry Hill coming out on top; and if only the few show exhibitors will persevere, increase in number, and produce a clean, well-marked, and above all, roomy sheep, the future of the Kerry Hill as an attractive commercial proposition is assured.

It was by chance that I started with Kerries. When I needed to replace my first little nondescripts, Mr. George Lee, the Stratford-on-Avon butcher who bought my fat lambs, offered to buy me a pen of ewes at Craven Arms (advertised then as 'the largest ewe sale in England'.) Would I like to come with him one week and have a look?

41

It was a wonderful opportunity which I grasped, and we drove west with some of his farmer friends. Near Craven Arms the roads were filled from hedge to hedge with large bunches of sheep, driven in to market from neighbouring farms. Each lot was separated fore and aft by men, boys and dogs, and woe betide the car which tried to push through, making the sheep break forwards or back, and mixing the lots, so that an extra job of drawing had to be done in the sale yard by already time-pressed and frustrated men.

Trade was good the day we went: I fell for a second prize pen of registered Clun Forest two year olds, but Mr. Lee thought them too dear—he and his friends did not buy that day. A week or two later he sent me a pen of twenty unregistered Kerries—much cheaper, but they were a weak lot and I lost one or two even before lambing. I decided to buy on my own in future.

When Pa Pugh heard, through Bob and Ethel, that I had unregistered Kerries he sent a message to say why not add some registered ewes and breed pure, instead of crossing with a Suffolk? I replied that I was happy producing fat lambs, and anyway had no room to rear young ewes; but he persuaded me to try just a few, and his son Leslie, who was carrying on the Uphampton flock at Arley, in Worcestershire, brought me four two year olds in 'lamb to Uphampton Richie. In 1939 these ewes produced a ram and three ewe lambs good enough to show at the centenary Royal at Windsor. Leslie trimmed them for me, and came to Armscote again on the morning of departure for finishing touches, and to speed me off. I was met on the showground by Bob Jones, the Duke of Westminster's shepherd, who helped to unload and showed me the ropes. Next morning we were judged, and my ram lamb, Armscote Bomber, was second in his class and the ewe lambs were third in theirs. The Duke's yearling ram, Eaton Factor, so well brought out by Bob, was Kerry Hill champion, and we were all thrilled to bits. Those two prize cards hang framed in our loo today.

I was bitten properly by the showing bug. That autumn I cleared all my unregistered sheep, and bought, at Leominster ewe sale, the first prize pen of two year old Kerries from Mr. William Nicholls of the Hole Farm, Shobdon. On September 1st 1939, I drove up to the Flock Book Society's show and sale at Kerry, with the clouds of war hanging heavy upon us. Trade plummetted: my ram lamb Bomber, first in his class, was sold for nine and a half guineas; and I was able to buy, to head my flock, the Duke's Royal Champion, Eaton Factor for twenty-seven. Two days later war was declared, and that was the end of my showing without Mary. But I registered Number 611, the Armscote Flock, and became a breeder of pedigree Kerry Hill sheep.

As things turned out I had plenty of room to rear young ewes at Buckley Green. I sold them each year at Craven Arms, although it was the 'wrong way' to move. (The theory is that breeding stock should be sold always from west to east or north to south—from higher and poorer to lower and richer land.) Mine might have sold as well or better at Stratford, for parts of Buckley Green were higher and poorer than many a Welsh Border farm; but I longed to go west, to keep my flock in the eye of the Kerry Hill breeders, and anyway to go from home at all was an adventure in war-time. Lorries were travelling empty from the Midlands each week to bring loads from the Border sales, so my transport costs were not too high. I had many a good day out, and the sheep trade boomed.

In 1943 came the cut-back and my move to Kingsland. The rigorous culling was good, and I gathered together again about twenty really nice ewes of my own breeding. Soon after Mary joined me we were lambing between thirty and forty, and aiming to sell the best twenty-five Kerry Hill two year olds at Craven Arms each year. We won first prize four years running, from 1951 to 1954. In 1955 we reduced again and went to America.

The relief of having Mary to share the lambing was immense—ten years of sleepless March nights had taken their toll. Now we were able to watch on alternate nights, with one going thankfully to bath and bed in the house, the other, fully dressed, taking cat naps on a camp bed in the buildings. There was agreement that the one off

Craven Arms, 1954. Mr. Richard Barker presenting 1st. Prize ribbon for best 25 ewes

would always come in emergency, but the one on duty hardly ever called—it was a matter of principle to manage if one could, though never at the cost of a life. The night's triumphs and disasters were told through the bedroom window in the morning while the one off drank her thermos cups of tea in bed.

We lambed the ewes outside until the last few years of our time: they were driven gently out each day to one or other of the larger meadows, kept fresh all winter, so that they had regular steady exercise, even in snow; at night they returned to their hay in the small paddock by the buildings. We put out the hay in their absence, using double-sided wheeled cratches, at least one for every ten ewes, to avoid pushing and crowding; the cratches were moved their own distance daily. We were lucky in the well-drained Kingsland ground and did not suffer too badly with muddy gateways, though there were always lame ewes to dress as soon as they had lambed. This was done, and the udders checked and cleaned, in small pens dotted around the buildings. In bad weather we carried in the lambs almost as soon as they were dropped, held by the fore legs with the rear dangling under the nose of the anxious mum. She was supposed to follow closely, but sometimes broke back, plunging through the crowd to look for the other lamb which as often as not was still inside her. Alone in the dark, with a cold wet lamb, we dreaded these desperate journeys, but the straw haven was reached at last and we usually had a pair of lambs ready to greet the partner in the morning. We used to pray for quiet fine nights when you could prowl through the sitting sheep with no-one moving and a myriad twin jewels of eyes glittering in the torch light. Then it was easy to see when someone took herself apart under the hedge, sickening to lamb. She would be watched through the night—important to know how long she'd been at it and when she needed help. One of the nightmares was to lie for an hour's nap and return to find her standing miserably, with a lamb's head hanging out and no feet to be seen. Then she must be stalked from behind till near enough to thrust torch in pocket and make a dash, hands clutching the wool on either flank, hanging on, trying to keep one's feet, dragged a few yards till she packed up and could be eased to the ground; the lamb's head was pushed back, front feet found, and a safe delivery made. If the head is there and the time is not too long the lamb is usually alive—it's with a breech presentation that they drown so quickly.

The normal pattern of lambing is for the ewe to sicken, scraping the ground and turning restlessly about for an hour or so till the water bladder comes, when she will lie and strain, a head and two front feet will appear, and soon afterwards the lamb should be born: a bit of help here is invaluable, because the quicker he comes the quicker he will suck and gain strength—a long struggle by himself may mean a weak lamb. The joy is to look at the flock after a quiet hour, expecting nothing, and find a ewe suckling two strong lambs in the darkness. It happens quite often with Kerries.

When it is impossible for a ewe to lamb she knows it, and will not try. She may stand about miserably for hours (or even days, when dead lambs result)—it's important to know when to intervene. Nowadays farmers will take such a case to the vet, and leave her with him till he has time to lamb her. In our day this was not thought economic sense, and in our case the trauma of such a journey was too great, so we coped ourselves. One of us scrubbed up, the other lowered the ewe gently on to the clean straw, and the right hand and arm, drenched in antiseptic oil, slid gently into those infinitely mysterious swimming depths. Eyes screwed tightly shut, we would talk to each other and the ewe—'a tangle of legs here, but no head yet ... is this a hock or a knee?' There could be twelve legs—to which head do they belong? Sort them gently against the massive straining of the ewe, hand pressed into the lambs, sharp hocks straightened and tiny cloven hooves guarded lest they rip the wall of the womb. At last, after an hour maybe, a pair of front legs, followed by the right head float by magic into the passage and the first new-born lamb is drawn out alive. The relief and joy are indescribable. We soon have him under the ewe's nose, the busy tongue licks while the right hand goes in again to search once more. This time it is easier, but one of the three comes out backwards and is dead; the third almost delivers itself and is alive. The lambs are slapped and dried and suckled, lying against the belly of the weary ewe; but soon she is helped to her feet, the lambs rise up, she receives a shot of penicillin, and a day or two later she runs out with a fine pair of twins. It doesn't always work out like that but when it does it's a miracle on top of the eternal miracle of birth.

Ewes with new-born lambs spent a few nights in the pens, depending on the weather and strength of the lambs: they ran out by day in the Little Orchard, returning to a small feed—as they reached the buildings they would fan out and select their own pen of the night before—sheep are sensible animals if not harried; each ewe knows how many lambs she should have, and is not content with two when it should be three. Directly after birth the lambs' navels were immersed in iodine; we carried in the pocket a small jar and some iodined tapes, in case of bleeding. The first morning after birth each

46

lamb was weighed and numbered. The heavy burden carried by pregnant ewes amazed us—single lambs (not many of those) averaged 12lb, with an occasional 14 and a recorded top of 18lb; while a belly full of twins, triplets or quads could total 27lb, and then there was also the fluid and the placenta. No wonder the ewes were slow getting about! We weighed on a platform machine, taking our own weight first and then receiving a lamb in our arms—a danger here, because once a lusty lamb struggled so violently that my arm tightened too hard and must have broken a rib. At first we couldn't think what was the matter with him and nursed him for a fortnight, but he died in great pain in the end. It was a hard lesson which showed the sense of the front leg carrying custom, to protect the fragile rib cage.

Numbering the lambs to record their pedigree was done by ear notching with a small leather-punch. Our code was alternate holes and notches going clockwise round the ear, digits in the left, tens in the right. Sometimes the punch would cut a tiny vein, there was blood all over the place and the wounded ear would flop. Then we'd be anxious that it would never recover and the sought-after sharpness would be lost—but it never was. A minor hazard, but my life is spent in such anxieties! Mary is always reassuring.

After some years lambing around the buildings many of the young lambs developed a dangerous scour: at about twenty-four hours old they would stop sucking and pass a whitish fluid, straining with little cries of pain. The remedy was half a small sulphamethezine pill, slid down the throat with a forefinger. We kept them alive with teaspoons of white of egg beaten up with a little whisky until they could suck again. We didn't lose many, but it weakened them terribly and after a second season of this we decided to leave the buildings and lamb down the ground.

For three years we set up lambing pens in a different small field each year: they were built with straw bales and hurdles, roofed with a rick sheet. In mid-field was a four wheeled stubble poultry house in which we had reared chickens; this now contained a camp bed. The worst part of the whole thing for us was setting out at 10 p.m., in dark and driving rain or snow, to trudge three fields, weighed down with heavy baskets full of thermos flasks and hot water bottles. Gone was any hope of calling the partner in emergency; but it always felt better when you got there, to the greeting of the gleaming eyes. My narrowest shave was early one morning: two ewes were lambing together—I was attending to one, but the other lambs had not risen when a carrion crow alighted and hopped towards their eyes. I was just in time to stop the fatal peck, but it shook me a lot. The last straw was a vicious easterly gale at the end of March 1952 which ripped the roof off the pens. We had nearly finished lambing and returned to the buildings; but the move had done the trick, and we had no more epidemics of scour. In after years we lambed the ewes indoors in a purpose built barn, with the luxury of electric light and no more blind dashes to catch in the dark.

After the pens the ewes and lambs moved on fast to fresh ground, and the ever-growing twice daily count began. There used to be a superstition that the shepherd never counted lambs till tailing time, when he received his bonus per tail; but of course we knew our count and it was exciting as the tally mounted over the expected lamb and three-quarters. Our most prolific ewe was Mrs. Trip, who had eighteen lambs in seven years, of which thirteen were ewes, including a quad., all female. More later of Mrs. Trip.

'Sheep should never hear the church bells twice in the same field' and we held fast to the old saying, moving them on weekly even if the change was to less grass—the ground would have freshened. Moving ewes and lambs was quite a performance, as with them went their feed troughs—enough for thirty or forty ewes to feed comfortably, with extra room for lambs, who soon began to poke in for a bite; and also the open-ended tea chests, which we dotted all over the field on their sides, backs to the wind. We collected these large light plywood boxes from grocers for free. They lasted ages—we still have some—and were a priceless boon—easy to swing round against the wind and light enough to do no harm if blown over. In bad weather there might not be a lamb on the field—they were all

Mrs. Trip with her 1949 triplet ewe lambs

couched serene in their kennels until someone thought it time to suck, when there was a clatter of hooves on wood and a torrent of lambs poured forth, each to a never far distant mum. It was a witty sight which we loved.

The season's round of sheep handling was soon in full swing — worming, vaccinating, foot rotting, tailing, washing, shearing and dipping. The vaccinations were chiefly against pulpy kidney disease, though as time went on multi-vaccines were developed. The lambs are protected for a few weeks after birth by an injection to the ewe a month or so before lambing. We always hated penning and handling heavy in lamb ewes, and never threw them: if their feet also needed attention they were treated standing up. The lambs were vaccinated in conjunction with their first worm drench at about six weeks old;

we hated this operation too, plunging a needle into tender skin and trickling fluid into little fighting mouths. Mary did all the injections—she became expert—and usually I did the drenching.

Foot rot is a contagious disease living in the soil: it was always with us, and was worst in wet weather, when the hooves were soft. The treatment was to pare the horn with a sharp knife and dress the foul-smelling rot with an abrasive, such as copper sulphate or butter of antimony mixed with Stockholm tar—a messy job, and the chloromycetin spray which was developed later was a great relief.

We made permanent handling pens in a corner of the paddock adjoining the road and running alongside the walls of the building, with swinging gates leading into the dipping and foot baths. Old Ren dug out and concreted the deep dipping bath, and a splendid job he made of it. A tap piped through the wall supplied water but there was no way of emptying it except by hand. We bucketed out hundreds of gallons into the two-wheeled water cart, pulled it back through the pens and tipped it through the road hedge into the ditch, whence it must have soaked into the nearby brook. The dip was changed two or three times a year, but there was never a complaint from neighbours, and hardly a thought from us until the enormity of the pollution began slowly to dawn. By then it was too late to remedy—we were moving and the dip became redundant; but it may not have done lasting harm as the silver birch tree we planted near the pens for much needed shade flourished and is now a beautiful tree—one of the few of our planted trees at Brook Farm which has survived the chain saws of those who followed us.

Compulsory double dipping, summer and autumn, was in force through some of our time, but it was dropped in the 1950's and many outbreaks of sheep scab followed. We would have dipped twice anyway, the first one (with DDT, now banned) to protect against fly strike, the second (Border Liquid) to clear the ewes of ticks and lice before tupping. Fly blow before shearing was a menace, though the advent of the knapsack sprayer made things easier; but our hearts would sink when the shepherd of the hour reported 'Pearl or

Elizabeth or whoever—has grubs.' The twist and nibble of a 'struck' sheep is unmistakable, and if you're in doubt she isn't! But we were suspicious of dirty twitching tails and the whole bunch must be gathered for a closer look. Tails can be trimmed with shears, but if the grubs are left in for many hours the skin will be cut and the mark will show all season; and if a struck sheep is missed, on moor or mountain, she can literally be eaten alive.

Washing before shearing is now a thing of the past; but when we started there was a difference of several pence a pound between washed and 'greasy' wool, and shepherds would grumble if they didn't have the easier shearing. The sheep must swim in running water, and in early summer the lanes would be full of driven sheep making their way to the temporary pens set up by farmers who were lucky enough to have a deep stream such as the rivers Lugg or Arrow, running through their land. We had the Pinsley Brook, but it was not ideal: there was one deep pool by which we set a platform on the bank. Arthur and Jim upended each sheep while one of us slipped round her neck a noose attached to a long pole. Then she was lowered into the water, guided to swim downstream and brought ashore to scramble up a low place in the bank; but the water was seldom deep enough for a satisfactory job, and one year, when it was very low, we had poor Jim, in borrowed waders, meeting the sheep in midstream and ducking them again. We were all thankful when we could abandon the job and sell unwashed wool with a good conscience.

Shearing we found physically our most demanding job. Mary had learned a little from Frank Roberts, and I from Tom Nicholls when he came to Buckley Green to help me after I bought his father's ewes. At first Mary and I sheared the show sheep and rams ourselves, while Arthur helped with the ewes; but Jim was a beautiful shearer, and we were very glad to hand over to him, and after him to Old Ren's son Desmond, also first rate, who travelled the district with a mate, contract shearing in the modern mode.

We took pride in presenting our clip well to the merchants. The weather must be fine for several days, so that the sheep were dry to the skin. Nowadays farmers shut them overnight in the large empty cattle sheds, but even today there is a price penalty for straw and muck in the fleece. Each sheep was turned on her backside on to a low wide wooden bench, polished a rich brown with the rub of the greasy wool: the fleece fell away in one piece from a good shearer onto a clean concrete floor. There was no desperate dash to shear a sheep every two minutes, so that lumps of wool and ugly cuts were left; but the long rhythmic 'blows' down each side were a joy to watch, and in four or five minutes a beautifully patterned sheep rose up and ran back to the pens. Then the shearer would gather the fleece and toss it flat, onto a tarpaulin, where Mary would 'lap' it up inside out into a tidy ball, secured with a long coil of its own neck wool. The merchant's wool sheet, a large long hessian bag, like a mattress cover slit down one side, was slung up with cords to the rafters in the building hard by; each fleece was packed straight in, before it had time to pick up bits, and when the sheet was full, with about twenty to thirty fleeces averaging 8lb each, the side was sewn up with a bagging needle threaded with special waxed string supplied by the merchant, because binder twine must never come near wool lest it shed fibres into the fleece. Mary did all this work and was very good at it.

In the early days we hauled the bulky wool sheets on a dray to Kingsland station, whence they went by rail to Worcester. The Wool Board was the buyer and it was illegal to sell privately, as it still is; but the clips were graded by merchants, and when we started showing, our wool buyer selected our best three or four fleeces and slipped them back in time for us to take to the first show. When the show season was over we took these fleeces up to Mr. and Mrs. Leach at their old woollen mill at Mochdre, near Newtown. Here they were woven with the spidery machinery into beautiful rugs and blankets— two fleeces to a blanket. We are using still two rugs labelled 'Over-all champion Three Counties 1955' and '1st Prize Royal Show 1958'.

V
Showing—The Setting

Showing is a way of life and those who follow it become addicted. I got the bug at the 1939 Windsor Royal, and as soon as possible after the war we started again together.

There were the 'Big Shows', where you stayed away from home, and the 'Locals', crammed each into one hectic day. The 'Big Shows' for us were the Shropshire and West Midland, two days in mid-May; the Bath and West and the Three Counties, three days each in June; the Royal, most of a week in early July; and the Royal Welsh, three days at the end of July. The 'Locals' went on through August and the first weeks of September, when they gave way to sheep sales, and summer was gone.

The difficulties of getting away were many, but we managed. With the Shropshire and West Midland the worry was—could we get the cattle turned out of winter quarters by then? In 1955 we stayed, in a fierce May snow storm, to fetch them all back under cover again. We drove to Shrewsbury on icy roads very early next morning, with little time in hand to settle the sheep before judging at 10. On the way we found the Court Llacca lorry upside down on Dorrington railway bridge. Mr. Eckley, Robert and the sheep were shaken, but all right. We plied the humans with hot coffee from our thermos flask and drove on. A breakdown gang righted their lorry and they followed, late but triumphant, to head their Clun Forest classes as usual, while we too managed to have our Kerries before the judge on time.

53

Yearling ewe, Bath and West Show, 1958

The Bath & West in early June was always awkward for shearing—should we rush it through before we went, when perhaps the weather would be too cold, or leave it till our return, with the risk that the full-fleeced sheep could be 'struck' by the blowfly and get maggots in their wool? We usually chose to shear later, but sprayed the whole flock before we went.

With the Three Counties in mid-June the worry was the first cut of hay—before or after? (It nearly always thundered in Three Counties week!) Before the Royal, first week in July, we would try desperately to haul the current field of hay before leaving: but by the Royal Welsh, end of July, surely hay harvest was finished and our merry mood matched that of the Show.

Shows have their own atmosphere: the communities of animals and stockmen come and go, much the same, but the feeling of each show was different. In our early years the only one with a permanent show ground was the Shrop. and West Mid., set in a bend of the Severn by Shrewsbury. We camped right on the river bank, with the town lights twinkling on the other side, and in the early morning swans, and the occasional sculler, slipped by. It was a solid, dependable show—you knew what you were coming to—and full of interest, with its young animals, first time out, a criteria for the season's form. The Bath and West, which ranged across the West Country from Plymouth to Cardiff, was beautifully organised, with always a courteous welcome. The Three Counties, on a different site each year in Herefordshire, Worcestershire or Gloucestershire, was familiar and friendly. The Royal, with its red tape and old school ties, produced in me more butterflies in the tummy than any other show; but we felt enormous pride and loyalty for it. The Royal Welsh in those days was random beyond belief—we found our pens standing in water one year, but full of fun and friendliness, as it is now on its splendid permanent show ground at Builth Wells.

First Three Counties Show at Malvern, 1958

One by one the shows were forced to turn to a permanent ground. The costs of a temporary site became prohibitive, with the laying of sleeper roads, water and electricity lines, and the erection of acres of canvas buildings, so vulnerable to weather. In 1962, when the Royal was on the Town Moor at Newcastle, a fierce gale in the previous week flattened the cattle tents, tore the tops off the sheep pens and virtually destroyed the stock lines. Much was made of this in the national press and the Council of the Royal were afraid that their exhibitors would not turn up. After superhuman efforts they were able to send a telegram to every stock exhibitor: 'We are ready for you—please come'. This was received on the Saturday morning, but we missed ours, having started already; we travelled always to the Royal before the weekend to give the sheep time to settle. Fortunately we had loaded all the canvas sheets we possessed; the reassuring telegram made many leave theirs behind. When we arrived, late in the evening after the three hundred mile drive, we found our pens still open to the skies—we worked till after midnight rigging up sheets to roof them, and were never more thankful to bed down in the lorry, and to lie late and enjoy a leisurely Sunday before the busy sheep trimming Monday—in those days the Royal opened to the public on a Tuesday.

There was seldom a parking problem on these large and often beautiful temporary sites—stockmen put their vehicles where they pleased in the parking area. Some liked to be near their stock and cheek by jowl with their mates: we preferred to be a bit remote, avoiding noisy late night parties in adjoining lorries and enjoying the longer walk to and from the sheep lines. Sometimes we had the luck to find wonderful spots—at the Bath and West at Swindon a nightingale sang close to the lorry, and at the 1954 Royal in Windsor Great Park (in our diary 'best of the lot') a hen pheasant and her chicks busied about near our feet as we sat in deck chairs beside the ramp.

But then, to the Royal, came Mr. X, and the carefree peace was shattered. We were aware of him first at Nottingham in 1955. He was chief executive of the newly employed car-parking firm, and he was affronted by the random parking of the livestock exhibitors. He could not understand the homely set-ups, with beds and boiling kettles in the lorries. He did not realise that, once set, a furnished lorry with crockery on the table was perilous to move—people sat staring at him, and didn't. He had to give up!

By 1956, at Newcastle, he had found his feet. He walked up the hill on the Town Moor to where we were parked near the Show Yard muck heap, with a magnificent view of the Show below. He asked what we were doing there, but had neither reason nor authority to move us. His attitude was unpleasant, and left a nasty taste.

The following year of the great thunderstorm at Norwich, he excelled himself. He must have the stock lorries in lines, radiator to radiator, 'because it looks better from the air'. He went from lorry to lorry, urging and cajoling; no-one moved. When we waved to friends as they drove in, he ran to us shouting 'They can't park near you'. We had our dog Flax with us; he was terrified with the thunder; and Mr. X threatened us with the police and involved the officer at the gate ('No dogs on the showground'). We went straight to the secretary of the Royal, Alec Hobson, who was charming, and confirmed that dogs in the lorry park were quite all right so long as they did not come on to the showground. Everyone knew this rule without the help of Mr. X. But it was a miserable show, and he riled so many people that an exhibitors' petition was sent to Royal H.Q. in London. After that Mr. X kept a low profile and shunned the lorry parks.

The long-considered choice of Stoneleigh Abbey as a permanent site for the Royal was of great interest to us. The first Show there was in 1963, but we had an inkling that something was afoot several years earlier, when Anne Leigh limped from Show H.Q. to see us in the distant sheep pens as we trimmed on the Monday before opening day. Robin Leigh was senior steward of the Grand Ring for many years, a familiar figure on a grey cob, riding ahead of the Royal Procession as it drove round the Ring to the Grandstand.

I was at school and college with Anne Hicks Beach as she then was, a merry laughing figure with dancing eyes. She was good at lacrosse and we played together in the Dartford Physical Training College first XII, she attack and I defence; the gleeful grin with which she took a pass and slammed the ball into goal gave me many a thrill. Robin often came to Dartford from Sandhurst to court her—he had been at Eton with her brother William. Anne and I moved on together from school at Aldeburgh to Dartford in 1926, where we worked intensely hard for two years, though why Anne chose such a career I can't imagine—she would never have been a physical training mistress in a girls' school; but in the summer holidays of 1928 she had the ghastly accident which entirely altered her life. She was riding in the woods of the Hicks Beach home in Gloucestershire when her horse shied, throwing her heavily against a tree. Her leg was badly broken high up, near the hip. There followed years of pain, frustration and immense courage: the fracture did not heal, and after several operations a bone graft from the other leg was tried. The graft was successful, but the good leg went wrong and was amputated below the knee.

Robin stuck to her through thick and thin. She married him from a wheelchair, bore him four sons and they had the fun together of an Army family in pre-war days, with some hunting in Ireland when she was able to whip hounds in to him from a specially made offside saddle.

Then Robin inherited, they became Lord and Lady Leigh of Stoneleigh and shouldered the heavy responsibilities of a great estate. A disastrous fire devastated one wing of the Abbey and did damage they could ill afford to repair. They needed to plan new ways to carry on their place, and were able to agree with the Royal Agricultural Society of England for a permanent showground at Stoneleigh, later to be extended and developed as the National Agricultural Centre. Anne was sad for her newly planted avenue of young trees, which had to give way to roads and buildings.

At the first Stoneleigh Royal in 1963 she came as usual to the sheep pens, with a warm invitation to a bath and supper at the Abbey. (In all the years after she never failed to send a messenger.)

She was on two sticks by then, and her wrists as well as her legs were feeling the strain. We went early that first time, and she was able to show us part of the Abbey before her other guests began to arrive from their various jobs on the Showground. We had not realised then the extent of the house party and the famous Thursday night suppers. Robin would come in late from the Ring, often with muddy boots and breeches. The Windsor Greys were in the stables and the Crown Equerry, Colonel Sir John Miller, stayed in the house; so too did ladies and gentlemen of the Royal Household, and we were often entertained with domestic details, such as the time Prince Phillip would want his bath and where the Queen would meet Anne's disabled old folk if it was too wet for them to sit in their wheelchairs on the lawn; but in all the years we never saw any domestic staff—Anne met us at the door as we walked in unannounced; drinks were in the sitting room and a wealth of cold food was on the diningroom table. Conversation was uninhibited and great fun.

With Flax at the Shropshire and West Midland Show, 1954

The first time we were quite unprepared for such an occasion; but we always brought with us a supply of freshly laundered white coats, a clean one for each show day, to wear over our tidy shirts and trousers. We thought the most suitable thing to do was to wear Friday's coat for the Thursday supper party; so we kept the most pristine one for that, and have always hoped that Anne and Robin did not think us discourteous. One of the ladies was vastly amused by our attire, and said in the nicest possible way that she thought it was 'original'!

It was lack of time and energy, rather than of room, that brought us to shows without a change into mufti: by the first Stoneleigh Royal we had reached the acme of comfort and convenience in our transport, with caravan towed behind lorry. To our first Royal together, at York in 1948, we went in the old Standard saloon, towing a two-wheeled trailer roofed with canvas. In the back of the car, with the seat out, was tied the senior ram, and in the trailer, with a dividing board, were three yearling ewes and four lambs. The car boot, wide open and piled to the roof, carried bags of corn and mangolds, buckets, bedrolls and all our trimming gear, hay nets, and personal belongings: it seemed a very long journey. On arrival we settled the sheep in their pens, mucked out the trailer, littered it with fresh straw ready for home, and unrolled our bedding on top of that. We parked as close as possible to the canteen and loos—there was no separate park for stock vehicles in those days—and slept in our clothes side by side, ramp down and heads outwards—there were plenty of 'wakey-wakey' cries in the morning, and lots of rain, but we survived unscathed.

The following year we bought a pony-sized four-wheel 'Rice' trailer, but we could not ask the car to pull that. We needed a second vehicle, and were lucky to find, going cheap at £186 and 8 shillings, an ex-Army personnel carrier, with bullet proof cab and four new tyres. Tons of armour had been pulled off the back with the bus-like seating space, but the remaining square box of a cab was still heavy, hideous and most uncomfortable. We fitted an old car seat beside the driver, but the space was such that the passenger (Mary) had to

Dilly, Flax and Fly

sit sideways, back to the kerb. Exhaust fumes wafted up through gaps in the floor boards, and the engine was noisy and extremely slow; but it never let us down, and we crawled successfully round the country for several years. We called the vehicle 'Dilly'—she was made by the Standard Motor Co., a great name in those days, and we believe the Army had a fleet of them. 'Dilly' certainly came back from the War all right!

Meanwhile we had swapped the old Standard car for a new Vauxhall Velox, found that too grand, sold it privately very well indeed, and invested in a new Morris van, a splendid vehicle which served as private car and farm run-about for over ten years. We fitted a ramp for the back which also slotted in as a dividing board, and with a grid behind the front seats and plenty of straw, it was a most comfortable transport for rams or calves, sold singly in market. It towed the caravan on the rare occasion of a brief holiday near York, when we were visited by the police as we undressed in the caravan in a grassy lay-bye—'Suspicious characters had been reported transferring goods from a van to a caravan'. We were soon able to convince them that we were okay, but it shook us, and we didn't enjoy the trip.

In 1952 we decided to part with Dilly and the trailer. We ordered a new three ton Bedford lorry chassis, and Messrs. Vincent Greenhous of Hereford made a light stock lorry body to our design. The removable sides hinged down in one piece, needing for choice four of us to support them. Celia, the girl who worked for us at the time, used to get marooned underneath the slowly descending side, and emerged like a rabbit from the end of a tunnel, livening up the operation a lot! We stripped down only once a year, for apple harvest, when the clear bed of the lorry made a three ton load of bags easy: Jim and Arthur put them on, and we drove them into Bulmers, where the lorry bed and channel wall were level, making it easy to tip off the fruit. The lorry was lighter without its sides, but it was always a joy to drive, and we were glad when we could set it up again ready for next season's showing. With its varnished sides and

Yearling ewes, 1958

'Wenham & Elliott' in cream letters on the front it looked smart, and we were very proud of it.

The addition of the caravan marked the peak of our show transport. A small legacy enabled me to buy it, which I did at the Caravan Show in London, when I was there to judge the Kerries at the 1962 Smithfield Fatstock Show. It was a week of dense fog and I felt very much alone—but the caravan was a triumphant success, a home from home, and a safe refuge from the telephone in Brook Farm orchard. At the shows we were able to select our parking place, drop it off, and drive on to settle the sheep in their pens, returning to live in comfort without the chores of a muck out and setting up of beds.

The sheep travelled well in the lorry: they loved it, and once picked it out and loaded themselves in the middle of the Royal Welsh showyard at Machynlleth in 1954, when it rained in torrents all the week, the ground was a quagmire, and we did not dare to drive off the sleeper road to fetch them from the sheep pens. There were many wet shows, but that was the worst, closely followed by the Oxford Royal in 1950; but in all our thirty years of showing we never failed to get on or off a showground under our own steam, and we never had a breakdown, which says much for Arthur Kent and Doug Moon, both of Leominster, who serviced our vehicles throughout.

With plenty of room in the lorry we were able always to take a full team, an advantage financially perhaps, and certainly a good 'shop window'. The classes for Kerry Hill sheep in our time, both at 'Big' and 'Local' shows, were usually for: Ram—2 year old and over; Yearling Ram; Ram Lamb; three Yearling Ewes; three Ewe Lambs— so that a 'full team' totalled nine sheep; and we usually took two ram lambs, for company in their pen and for the fun for us of competing against each other. Ten sheep were a lot of work to prepare (only a pair of females are required nowadays) but a joy when ready, and we worked out a good management routine.

Showing—The Slog

Preparations began in January, weather permitting, when the rams and yearling ewes were brought in from the field and shorn; as the fleece fell away a coat was slipped on over the head and sewn firmly under the belly. The coats were made by Mary from heavy hessian cake bags lined with old blankets. The head holes were bound in broad braid, and there were braid straps for the sewing on. We tried to get the coats off after about a fortnight, as the neck holes tended to mark the fast growing wool; but they were well worth while to avoid the check caused by such early shearing.

The sheep were then housed in our purpose built pens on the yard. These were open on two sides, with a steeply pitched lean-to roof against the high brick wall of the granary. Old Ren thatched the roof for us, but heavy rain came through, so we laid galvanised iron sheets on top of the straw which made a well insulated covering. The open sides were blocked with straw bales in winter, leaving snug lying room with plenty of overhead air, an essential for housed sheep of any kind.

Twice daily exercise, with a bite of growing grass, was a 'must' for the show sheep: the ewes ran out across the concrete yard into the small paddock by the buildings, where they were supposed to stay about ten minutes, while the rams were driven down the concrete drive and along the hard road until we judged they had gone far enough, when they were allowed to graze on the varied grass verge. They were escorted by one of us with bike and dog, and it was interesting to watch their choice of grazing—the plentiful dandelions were favoured. Suddenly, usually far too soon, their heads would go up as they remembered the corn feed awaiting them, and they would set off hell-for-leather, galloping home down the centre of the road, with the biker riding merrily behind, and the good dog Flax running alongside; he would turn them if ordered to do so, but it was usually safer to let them go. Their swing across the corner as they cantered up the drive was madly dangerous, and would be out of the question these days; but then there were few cars, we were expected, and a cheery wave would greet our signal to slow down. Meanwhile the ewes in the paddock, if they had not arrived already, would have heard the hooves on the road and come full tilt to the gate, to be let in to the waiting feed, often arriving at the same time as the rams but always, after the first day, selecting the correct pen. Sheep are not stupid animals.

We mixed the sheep corn ourselves, basing it on rolled oats, broad bran and flaked maize (when obtainable—things were hard to get for several years after the war)—with additional small quantities of kibbled locust beans (like dates—sweet and hard), molasses meal, milk powder, mineral salts with vitamins, perhaps seaweed meal—anyway, plenty of variety. The show sheep feeds were measured in small handfulls and moistened at the last minute with a dollop of soaked sugar beet pulp, which had been covered in water for at least twenty-four hours. We gave six small feeds a day, counting the separate ration of chopped mangolds after the early morning corn; then corn after exercise, again at 1 and 5 p.m.; and last thing, about 10. Hay nets, filled lightly with the best possible hay, were available always, and of course, clean water, changed daily. It was important to hang the hay nets high enough to prevent an impatient foot from getting caught, yet low enough to avoid seeds falling into eyes or wool, or the sheep developing a hollow back from reaching up. The hay was freshened each evening and changed completely each morning. Corn and roots must be cleared within minutes of feeding—we were surprised at shows by the mass of food—chiefly roots—often left in front of sheep all day. There is a certain risk anyway in feeding mangolds to male animals, because the sugar crystals can cause a water stoppage; but in our quantities it was a risk worth taking for a juicy, much enjoyed feed. We carried to shows a chopping board with a swivelling knife, and with labour were able to chop the roots small; but when the big flock shepherds began to bring their hand turned pulping machines and stand them in the lines, we borrowed thankfully, nipping along with our whole roots to the Hamp. or Suffolk pens, turning a friendly handle, and back to the Hill sheep lines with a welcome bucket of freshly pulped mangolds. Folk were very matey and generous, and we were grateful.

At home the show sheep had the usual injections and worm drenches, but their feet needed little attention beyond horn paring to shape—they did not suffer from foot rot owing to dry standing and the regular exercise on hard ground. The main job was to turn them out well in the wool. Some weeks after shearing, when there was about an inch of new growth, we ran the machine up the backbone from rump to shoulder: if there was a dip in the back the wool was left longer at that point, to make it look level when trimmed to match. Then a stroke or two on either side of this strip would broaden the back as the wool grew; and a small stroke on the back of the tail, well below the rump, would square out the hind legs; the breech wool was left untrimmed and brushed up for shows. The sheep looked fun objects till the clean white scars assumed the same dirty colour as the surrounding wool! Their preliminary shaping was a tricky job and not strictly necessary, but it made trimming easier when the time came.

I learned to trim a little by watching Leslie Pugh prepare my lambs for the 1939 shows: he trimmed them for the Three Counties and the Royal, and then left me to it; but I had his base to work on, and only titivated. When Mary and I started again in '47 I did all the trimming at first, often making a right mess of it, but we both watched and questioned shepherds at the big shows—an advantage of going early—and received many valuable tips, and some lessons. When faults in beginners' work were apparent a competitor would even step in with his shears and alter things with a few strokes, to be beaten later on perhaps, by that same beginner! Such was the generosity, and the love of a good sheep well turned out, which we found in the show ring.

There are different fashions among the breeds: the Shortwools (the majority) aim at a compact fleece, trimmed close and level; but

Finishing touches at the Kerry Show and Sale, 1955

the Longwools are shown unclipped, and the Lincoln has his wool parted down the middle of the back to hang either side in separate ringlets, sometimes over thirty inches long: the skill and patience needed to do this work are amazing, but there is no trimming—nor on the Wiltshire Horn, who has no wool at all.

The exacting job of trimming began for us as soon as there was enough wool to shape the back, and continued almost weekly throughout the season, April to October: I was slow and allowed myself an hour a sheep. The lambs were not started till mid-May and then trimmed very lightly—Mary learnt on them, and soon took over from me completely. Their softer coats were more difficult than yearlings, but she soon excelled.

Before the shears come the carding combs, flat boards with a handle and fine wire bristles of different grades. The wool is worked up with a strong circular wrist movement, then lightly damped—I used a very wide paint brush for this—and the ends cut off with special long trimming shears until the required surface is achieved—or not! It is easy to notch the wool with an unsure hand.

Not less than a fortnight before the first show we washed the sheep all over with kitchen soap and lukewarm water, and then plunged them to rinse in the dipping bath, ready filled with clean water and a small amount of special show-sheep dipping powder, which left the wool looking live and creamy rather than the dead white of winter woollies. Washing at least two weeks ahead was important because it allowed time for the grease to rise again in the wool, so that it filled the judge's hand; but a nightmare of keeping clean and dry followed. Their pens at home were lined, and we took with us to shows a large pile of thirty to forty new beet pulp bags, each fitted with five sets of unfrayable string ties. The first job on arrival at a show, before unloading, was to 'bag the pens', to prevent rubbing on dirty hurdles. The nightmare was exercise at home, when a sudden shower would send one dashing to call in the ewes, while the other came back up the road with the rams even faster than usual. This anxiety persisted all summer, as the wool should not be soaked more than once in the season, to preserve the grease. The art was to keep the sheep looking fresh throughout—it was easy to be beaten at the Royal Welsh by a ram who had not been to the earlier shows.

We kept the once washing rule until disaster struck at the 1953 Royal at Blackpool. On the edge of the showyard, not far from the sheep lines, was a large expanse of rough ground, dotted with bushes and two or three small ponds. We took the ewes out there in the evening, where they grazed happily, thankful to be free; but on the Thursday, with another day's showing to go, one of them got a bite too close to the brink of a pond, the long grass gave way and in she plunged, struggled madly, churning up the shallow water, and emerged coated with slimy black mud! (Could this be why Blackpool is so called?) We hastened back to the sheep lines, where horrified friends saw us coming and were quick to catch the dripping black ewe before she reached her pen and rubbed the others. Willing hands held her, buckets of water were fetched and we washed her from top to toe, drying her after with every towel we possessed. I got up early next morning and carded and trimmed and trimmed and carded, until she nearly matched the others and the show ground began to fill with spectators. Blackpool was a memorable Royal!

Good presentation to the judge is a matter of pride, but also of particular importance in a breed like the Kerry Hill, where an alert presence and shining black and white markings are specially sought. Our show sheep were halter-trained as lambs, for they would follow their mothers willingly out to the field again despite the restraint of a leader beside them, while a difference of opinion was more easily resolved with a lamb than with a strong yearling. The older sheep were taught to stand proud but it was a mistake to overlead them, lest they got bored and dull. Breed points being equal, a sharp sheep will beat a dullard in the show ring; but the opinion of the judges is paramount on the day, and the exhibitor has entered with this agreement. Heated discussion and criticism at the ringside were nearly always rife but black looks in the ring were seldom seen—we all

Judging with Mr. Will Ward, Knighton ram show and sale, 1958

enjoyed ourselves. Some judges would delight in altering the plac-
ings at a previous show; others, especially with a large entry, would
get 'lost' and judge 'on the halter', knowing that so and so had been
an earlier winner. At one of the big Clun Forest shows and sales I was
at the ringside near a leading breeder, whose yearling ram had won
throughout the season: his shepherd was leading the ram while the
boss watched, with rising impatience, as one after another was called

in and placed, while the shepherd plodded on, round and round among the many others, until boss could bear it no longer. He vaulted the barrier, marched into the ring, took the halter from shepherd and at the next round was called in and sent to the top. I never heard the price afterwards, but Clun Forest champions made a lot of money in those days.

Judging is a thankless task, and I found it lonely. Perhaps it is pleasant to be the most important person in the ring, but the responsibility is great, and the post mortem round the pens, which the judge is expected to attend, can be very difficult. Some shows treat their judges with the utmost courtesy, conducting them to their ring and whisking them away to lunch when judging is over: the post mortem is mellower in the afternoon. Others can take little trouble: at a county show in far Wales, where I slept the previous night in the caravan on a runway of the vast disued airfield, I had to find my own way to the right ring in the morning, was abandoned by my steward after judging, and found the post mortem so heated that one of the exhibitors never spoke to us again because I placed his ewes fourth when he thought they should have been third. Our happiest memories of my judging are in Ireland: we flew together, once to Belfast, once to Ballsbridge, Dublin. At both places we found good entries of Kerry Hill sheep and the utmost warmth and hospitality from their owners, who drove us round their lovely country on the day after the show. We were so tired when we got back to Birmingham Airport late at night after Belfast that we slept by the roadside on the long drive back to Herefordshire, and again were questioned by the police. Our dark green van must have had a suspicious look!

Flock judging in October and November was another, much more pleasant experience. The Kerry Hill Flock Book Society ran a competition, with cups, for the best large medium and small flocks in the Book. The three winning flockmasters judged the competition in the following year. Our Armscote flock won several times the small class (twenty-five ewes or under) so one or other of us drove, with two varying companions, all over the country, visiting farms high and low,

Part of our flock, competition winners in 1950

and receiving always the utmost hospitality, which often made it difficult to fit in the scheduled number of visits in the day. When we travelled to see the Brudenells' flock in Northamptonshire we were bidden to stay the night at Deene Park, and this was indeed an experience. Deene is reputed to be the largest private house in England, and was the seat of the Brudenells' ancestor, the Lord Cardigan who led the charge of the Light Brigade in the Crimean War. A life size model of the horse he rode stands in the hall, with the actual mane and tail attached. The rooms at Deene are innumerable, but George and Tommy Brudenell made us feel entirely at home, with our own cosy quarters—mine were within a circular tower, with a small bathroom in the turret. We dined by candlelight, five courses with good wine, and conversation flowed. Next morning we looked out to see George setting off for London, complete with morning coat and stove pipe hat. Tommy gave us breakfast and delivered us to the waiting bailiff, who took us round the sheep. Tommy, a down-to-earth figure in blouse and skirt, received us back, gave us lunch and afterwards, when we ought to have been off, sat us down in the drawing room, exclaimed 'Just ten minutes nap, my dears,' clapped a newspaper over her face and was instantly asleep, while we sat quietly waiting. We agreed, as we drove out of the gates, that we had seen a rare slice of English life.

Our own small flock was the source of great pride to us: we kept careful records and the breeding lines were fascinating. We had one great ambition: to be supreme champion at the Royal *with our own breeding*. On the way there were many ups and downs, surprises and disappointments, but lots of fun. In the 1950's our great rival in the ring was Sydney Price of Cressage, a merry young man who brought his sheep out to perfection. To beat Sydney, as sometimes we did, was for us high honour, and any success was always a matter for congratulation between us, with never a hint of ill-feeling. Sydney is a compulsive competitor: he changed from showing Kerries to Cluns, where competition was fiercer, then on to Suffolks and still excelled. When at last he gave up sheep showing he concentrated on his dogs: for twenty-five years he competed in sheepdog trials all over the country until in 1987, at the age of seventy-one, he and his Davy triumphed by winning both English and International Trials in the same year. Sydney is a very popular 'one man and his dog'.

With the Kerries we beat him once with three grand yearling ewes which we were privileged to pick as lambs from the well-known flock of John Owens, the Woodhouse, Shobdon. 'Mr. John' (grandfather of the present John) was perhaps the best sheep man of them all, a kindly gentle man who had the amusing but perilous habit of suddenly popping his stick under his left arm as he bent to handle a sheep—woe betide the chap behind him! To this day we warn each other against 'doing a Mr. John'. We admired him greatly and remember him with affection when we pass the avenue of poplar trees which he planted alongside the Shobdon—Presteigne road just west of the Woodhouse.

Another exhibit of ours with which we beat Sydney Price was Mrs. Trip's triplets, who gave us more pleasure than any other sheep we bred. They were born in 1948, three perfectly marked, well grown ewe lambs, undoubtedly the best three we had that year. We showed them throughout—they were first at the Three Counties and in the money everywhere—it was huge fun. We had a terrific write up in the Hereford Times, and Mrs. Trip, herself no beauty, was a great

73

attraction too. She reared the three herself and accompanied us to the big shows—an arrangement economical in space and work, because normally we would have taken three ewes with the show lambs, and perhaps some non-show brothers and sisters as well. We were allowed to take suckling ewes to the early shows in those days, and would not have shown lambs otherwise. The Trips went on to be shown together as yearling ewes and Mrs. Trip excelled herself—she had eighteen lambs in seven years, including a quadruplet of ewe lambs whom we sold as a quad. of yearling ewes to found a flock in Somerset. Mrs. Trip ended her days with us.

It took us fifteen years to reach our showing goal: we had the female championship and reserve supreme, with yearling ewes, three times. At last, at the 1962 Newcastle Royal of the gale, our yearling ram Armscote Warrior won the supreme. We paraded him in the Grand Ring, the first time the sheep were privileged to be there, and went home proud and happy, to try again at Stoneleigh the following year.

1962: Armscote Warrior champion Royal, and son Yeast champion Three Counties

VI
Hereford Cattle

One day, before Mary joined me, I trotted home from Aymestrey Mill with Polly to the float, a low-loading two wheeled vehicle most useful for our corn hauling, though, with its doors and seat in place, I used it in Warwickshire as a get-about, to save the strictly rationed petrol. Polly went well to it and we were turning smartly into the Brook Farm drive when we found it blocked by a fair young woman leaning on a stick. I looked down the road from Kingsland and saw that it was filled from hedge to hedge with a magnificent herd of Hereford cattle—cows, calves, and heifers—their red coats and white faces shining in the sun as they moved slowly along. I pulled Polly across the bridge to stop them going up to Street, and watched them by with growing admiration. Veronica Corbett (as she was then) had just time to tell me, before hastening on to pilot them ahead, that she was moving her herd from her farm near Leominster, part of which had been commandeered for a prisoner-of-war camp, to the Ox House, Shobdon which she had just bought. I determined to press on with rebuilding my own pedigree herd to rival this new neighbour who became a lifetime friend.

When she left the Ox House in 1952 Veronica made a grand job of farming on her own in Gloucestershire. The Hill, Staunton, where she so kindly received our filly foal Jenny, was a rough, run-down two hundred acres: with the help of foreman Tom Hawkins and a good team Veronica turned it into a productive farm and a happy home. She introduced poultry and pig breeding units and took with her from the Ox House five of her best pedigree Hereford heifers. Her sheep at The Hill started with twenty Kerry and twenty Clun ewes which we bought for her at Knighton, two year olds to run with a Suffolk ram: there was little to choose between the resulting lambs but it was fun to test the rival breeds against each other.

Veronica's family grew up at The Hill and in 1965 she and Tony Sanger, whom she had married five years earlier, retired to live happily in Wiltshire until Tony's sad death three years later. Veronica then moved to a smallholding near Newent, where she bred riding ponies and helped the Ledbury Hunt Pony Club for many years.

There followed a time of great happiness, married to Anthony Taylor at North Aston in Oxfordshire. Anthony's death at Christmas 1985 was a heavy blow. The following year Veronica came back to Herefordshire to be near her family, who found for her the ideal smallholding, The Dukes Farm near Eardisley. It is only three acres but enough for her old pony mare, now retired after giving much fun to three families. Veronica has also the company of her lurcher bitch Bashful, a lovely tabby puss and in spite of these, the local foxes who play in broad daylight by the garden fence. It is happy for us all to have Veronica at The Dukes Farm.

At the Ox House Veronica's pedigree Herefords became well known and I had a long way to go. I started with two cows from Sidney Owens of Marlow: Prize Pansy 4th, who was bred by F.J. Newman in his famous Wickton herd; and Marlow Gay Lass, whose grandsire was Wickton Playful. Pansy came in calf to Tarrington Mainstay, and Lass to Tarrington Debonair. Sidney Owens was good enough to have them back to the same bulls the following year and the results raised us to the heights. Lass calved a beautiful heifer, Armscote Gay Lass, whom we showed later with success; and on 26th November 1945 Pansy gave birth to twin bulls, Duncan and David. Duncan looked the better of the two, and Pansy was not a heavy milker, so I sold David to Veronica, who had just lost a calf, and we concentrated on Duncan. Little did we think that one day Armscote Duncan would be the Hereford Supreme Champion at Sydney Royal Show!

Armscote Gay Lass, 3rd. Prizewinner at the Royal Show Shrewsbury, 1949

The time came when we needed a stud bull of our own, and in 1947 we set off to buy at the Hereford April Bull Sale. It was Mary's first outing after her accident, our first purchase together, lambing was nearly over and we felt in fine form. We had set our hearts on a Freetown bull and bravely bid on one; but he went into four figures and we had to give up. We were disappointed, he was a grand bull and we wanted one from Mr. Percy Bradstock's Freetown herd. Mr. Percy was a genial man who used to pull our legs regarding the food basket which we carried with us at bull sales—'always eating' was a regular joke between us. In the end we paid 200 guineas for Haven Just Fair, by Tarrington Mainstay, a nice young bull whose breeding looked just right for us. We called him Jeff and he did us very well; a quiet, sensible fellow like most Hereford bulls, he bred good cattle who made fair prices while the trade held; but in our small way we could never afford a top bull who, with good cows, might produce a record breaker.

We sold our young bulls as yearlings, usually at the Hereford spring sales when the market's horse chestnut trees were coming in to bud. All our calves were single suckled and weaned at about nine months, which gave us the winter to produce them for sale. They were fed much as the show sheep were, many times a day, with home mixed feed. At the beginning I had the good fortune to spend a day at the Ox House with Veronica's splendid Scottish herdsman Willie, to learn some tips—everyone has his own secrets, and it was a great privilege.

We haltered the best bull calves as babies, leading them out behind their mothers when we had time, and thus avoiding struggles with strong yearlings, which we could not manage. (There are dreadful stories of people tying bulls behind the tractor and driving on.) Then they soon learned to lead out for daily exercise as yearlings, first round the yard, then up and down the road. They were groomed thoroughly every day, washed before sale, and their horns were trained, to grow straight or slightly downwards, by small shaped lead weights fixed with straps across the forehead—these were worn for perhaps two weeks at a time and then removed or adjusted.

Horns can be dangerous in domestic cattle, who don't need them, and naturally polled breeds are a boon. De-horning (now general, with a compulsory anaesthetic) was painful, but we always rubbed the tiny horn buds of non-pedigree calves with a caustic stick, which killed the growth when done thoroughly. Since our day a group of bold and patient breeders developed a separate section of the Herd Book for naturally polled Herefords, crossing in with Red Angus and Galloway bulls, until the character was established. Fortunately the Hereford white face is always dominant, but it took time and money, and was a courageous enterprise which has paid dividends.

78

Our cattle had tidy horns, but we always took a chance, pushing in among five or six cows with calves in the little old covered yard where they lay at night, and climbing up the ever-rising muck with a skep of roots and corn on the hip, to spread it out along the manger in face of eager jostling cows. This was usually Mary's job—she was stronger than I. With hindsight we should not have given a morning feed, but put out a larger one for them to come in to at night; but the animals' welfare was always paramount, and we live to tell the tale.

There was one horn disaster, entirely unforeseen, with a nice young bull just ready for sale. It was lambing time and Mary's night off, and I marched in with his 10 o'clock feed to find him lying stone

Sheila with Armscote Duncan at Hereford Market, 1946

dead, with a broken neck. He must have been rubbing and caught the tip of his horn between the flimsy, unlined weather boards of the small loose box. The wrench to get free must have snapped his neck. I returned to the house and called up to Mary, who had gone to bed. We were deeply shocked—he was a good little bull and we were fond of him.

For a few years we averaged just over 100 guineas with yearling bulls at the sales. This was acceptable, and when the famous Captain de Quincey of the Vern gave 300 guineas for Armscote Duncan we were thrilled! We had watched 'The Captain' and his herdsman Don Gordon looking Duncan over before the sale but we never thought that he would want to buy; but he did, used him for a special breeding line, and later exported him to Australia for 3,000 guineas. There Duncan made a name for himself and our Armscote herd, and his supreme championship at the Sydney Royal was a triumph for us all.

'The Captain' was a legend in his time: he had a genius for pedigree breeding and every type of livestock in his care excelled. He bred exotic birds—we heard that they flew free in a bathroom— Sealyham terriers, Hackney horses and cattle—Beef Shorthorns and Herefords: de Quincey of The Vern was known all over the world.

We had the good fortune to be present at the dispersal sale of the Vern Herefords on the 17th October 1966, a day of warm sunshine and tense excitement. Leading breeders from Great Britain, Australia, the United States, the Argentine packed the tiers of straw bales round the open air ring at Marden, and when the auctioneer took his place on the rostrum the atmosphere was electric. Bill Gallimore of Messrs. Russell, Baldwin and Bright, extolled the historic occasion in a voice that almost broke with emotion; but it soon rose strongly to take the soaring bids for the beautiful cattle who passed serenely through the ring in the quiet hands of Don and Mrs. Gordon. The Gordons were in charge of the Vern bulls and brought them out to the nines. Mrs. Don in particular enhanced their appearance as she sailed majestically round the ring in white coat and snazzy hat of beret type: she sported a new one each season and with Veronica we watched in delight for the latest 'Paris model'.

The Vern sale totalled £231,000 for 136 lots, an average of £1,700 apiece. The highest price was made by a young bull called Vern Scorpio, who fetched 15,000 guineas from Major Symonds, of Llandinabo Court, buying for a partnership between Mr. George Wheelwright of San Francisco and Mr. Elwyn Jones of the Sheephouse, Hay-on-Wye. Last through the ring was a little old Dowager cow, probably too old for another calf: she was bought by an American breeder, and because he thought her too old to make the journey to the States, he presented her to the official artist of the Hereford Herd Book Society, Mrs. Barbara Turner ('Snaffles') who herself had a small pedigree herd. Such was the fitting end to a great dispersal sale.

In time we became disillusioned with our pedigree Herefords. Our two foundation cows each had one outstanding calf, Duncan and Armscote Gay Lass, whom we called Deb, to mark her sire, Tarrington Debonair. We showed Deb, with her first calf beside her, in 1949, when the Three Counties and the Royal happened to be close, at Leominster and Shrewsbury. We had far too much to do and it was a strain, but we were keen to achieve success with our own breeding and we did—she was second at the Three Counties and third at the Royal. The transport was hard work: we took Deb and her calf Godfrey first, settled them in, and then I came back for the sheep, leaving Mary to 'bag the pens'. We were lucky on both judging days to get the Kerries over before the Herefords were due; but it was an exercise not to be repeated.

Then came the dreadful disappointment with Deb: her second calf was a smashing bull who lived only a few hours—his breathing was wrong, and we felt sure that he had been crowded in the uterus because his mother was too fat after the previous season's showing. We failed to get her in calf again and in the end an ovarian cyst was diagnosed and she was sold for meat.

81

The two old cows, Lass and Pansy, came to the end of their breeding lives: Lass was put down at home by our good local knackers—her carcase made £15; but for Pansy, who was two years younger, we thought we ought to have meat price. We arranged to take her to the slaughter house ourselves, and to stay to see her kindly killed; but she slipped and fell to her haunches on the long way round from holding to stunning pen. Her head went up and I saw her eyes: I can see them still. (If the animal rights campaigners would turn their attention to what goes on in slaughterhouses, and to the export of live meat animals, they would save more distress and terror in more animals than the hunted fox.) We received £32 for Pansy: the price difference was pitiful but the difference in her end and that of Lass could not be measured in money.

The trade for Hereford crossing bulls was beginning to fall; after all the time and trouble it was deeply depressing to sell at little, if anything more than bullock price. We bred some nice heifers but had to sell one of the best for 200 guineas because we wanted the money. We could not afford, nor did we want, a posh herdsman to manage the cattle and us—we needed the joy of the stockmanship ourselves. After much thought, and with sadness, we decided to sell out of pedigree Herefords and turn to suckled calf rearing; but it was a grand thought that we could give even more time to the sheep, our Number One Priority.

VII
Retrenchment

Arthur's tenancy of Hill Farm marked a turning point for Jim. He missed the tractor trips up to Lucton and the shared work, ploughing all day on the hill for Arthur to follow with the mares; and he missed the company and comradeship at The Brook, for although Arthur came often to help, the commitment and shared responsibility were not the same. Also, Jim hated working a horse.

When Arthur took over at Hill Farm he bought himself a little old 'Fergy' tractor and had no need for horses. Our grey mare Lester was old too: I bought her ten years before at Craven Arms sale under the kind eye of 'Mr. Nicholls the Hole'. She was a splendid creature, almost white with nutmeg flecks and a pink nose, very active, but calm and sweet. We had a great sadness with her, because we got her in foal to a Shire yet worked her too long into the spring, and after a long day 'bouting out' for potatoes she slipped a beautiful little filly who lived only a few days—Lester had no milk and the Duggans could not rear the foal. It was before Mary joined me—I was tied at Kingsland and could not get to and fro often enough to help with the suckling. I reproach myself bitterly for a gross lack of thought.

Arthur could not keep Lester so she was put down quietly on the farm; but the bay mare Dolly we kept, with some implements, to work with us at the Brook. She was a light draught mare, like Lester, but with Welsh cob in her no doubt—I bought her from a farming neighbour of Veronica's mother near Abergavenny. She was a splendid worker, with a good fast walk but with rather an anxious temperament. Mostly we worked her ourselves, but the good boy Graham used her, under our eye, for muck hauling with the cart. Dolly was able to back with great accuracy but when the load was unbalanced she hated the pressure of the belly band and would nab at the arm of the guiding bridle hand. When we took her over from Graham he always said 'Mind she doesn't bite you!' We quote him to this day when a warning sentence begins with 'Mind!'

Jim did not like Dolly, and used her seldom; but one wet winter we grew a patch of marrow stem kale which was cut each morning and hauled out to the cows and calves. Horse and cart made less mess than tractor and trailer and was easier for one man to manage when the horse would stop and start to command; so Jim used Dolly for this job and they both hated it. Dolly was fratched by the crowding cattle and Jim was fratched by her extra starts and stops. We hated it for both of them; but when Jim remarked to me, in his usual quiet way, that it was a miserable job on a cold wet morning, I replied, with more thought for animals than human, that we were jolly lucky to have the kale to feed—a massive insensitivity.

In April 1953 Jim was rushed to hospital with acute appendicitis: after the operation he seemed never to pick up properly, and though he worked on steadily for us for another eighteen months, the old zest was gone, and in December 1954 he told us he was returning to Westhope, whence he had come: one of his reasons for leaving was 'I didn't come here to work horses'. He had given us nearly five good years and we were grateful; but it was an awful blow. We never had a cross word, have been in touch with him since, and remain good friends.

Charlie followed Jim at Brook Bridge—a true, steady boy who served us well, but he had neither the experience nor the skills of Jim. We found ourselves with far more work and more responsibility, and we were very very tired. We cast in our minds how to reduce: we had decided already to sell the pedigree Herefords, and we longed to concentrate our energy on the sheep; but we badly needed a break.

We consulted with Frank Roberts, whose Ledicot land adjoined our Brook meadows. We discovered that he would like very much to add a small dairy unit to his mixed farming enterprise: if we would provide the capital for a milking parlour he would do the work, which included a great deal of concreting and earth moving to make holding yards: he would rent from us Brook Bridge, with its house, buildings and 45 acres, which would leave us with Brook Farm as a smallholding again, but now, with all our added bits, made up to 42 acres. We were worried about Charlie, having moved him and his small family into Brook Bridge only a few months before; but Frank Roberts would take him on as cowman if Charlie wished. We wondered about our hay-making, with no regular man and no tractor: we could hire a contractor to bale and Frank would haul for us. (The prospect of his six man team whipping our bales into the buildings was rosy indeed.) We would manage the making with Dolly, our pikles, and sometimes Arthur's help. We would be saved the rising wages of a full time man and have a basic income from the rent. Above all, we would be saved the work and worry of more acres than we could manage, and the land would be properly farmed. After

Armscote Herefords at Brook Farm, 1953

much thought and searching discussion about terms, we agreed that Frank should take over Brook Bridge at Michaelmas 1955.

We thought on, and decided to hold an auction sale on the farm—a dispersal of the Herefords, a reduction of the sheep, some implements and all the pigs: with over thirty cattle and a drastic culling of the sheep, it was a good catalogue. Frank Roberts hauled in straw bales and built us a tiered cattle ring in the Brook Bridge barn. There was a pleasant crowd of buyers and prices were very satisfactory. We planned to spend part of the proceeds on a long holiday.

The year after we showed Mrs. Trip's ewe lambs we received a letter from America: it was addressed 'Wenham & Elliott, Herefordshire, England', and was written by Marian Gelsleichter, a hospital nurse then working in New York City. Marian was near retiring to her inherited smallholding in Massachusetts, and had seen in the New York Herald Tribune a write-up about the triplet lambs and us: she wondered whether we could sell her some in-lamb ewes to found a flock of Kerry Hill sheep at Tyringham. Thus began a correspondence which lasted until just before Marian's death in 1987, and included, in the early days when we were still rationed, wonderful parcels of sugar and goodies and many a warm invitation to visit her and Bill and see for ourselves the farm Craholla.

Three times we tried to export pregnant ewes: the first year was no good because of an outbreak of foot and mouth disease somewhere in Britain; the second time the sheep were actually in quarantine when the United States clamped down on all sheep imports until the debilitating disease scrapie was eliminated from Great Britain;—it is rare, and none of us hereabouts had ever met it, but that ban continued for years. In the end we again had the sheep ready for Marian when a new regulation shortening the period when pregnant ewes might travel came into force, and ours could not meet it. By this time we were browned off, especially by the poor condition in which our sheep were returned from the ministry quarantine station. When the opportunity came for us to travel we suggested ourselves instead to Marian and were welcomed with all the warmth in the world.

We planned to be away about ten weeks, October to December 1955, staying partly with Marian and Bill but also travelling around to see as much of the country as we could on the strict dollar rationing then in place. Ten weeks seemed quite a stretch to leave our animals in other hands, but we were fortunate in having Helen Wasdell working for us at the time. Helen lived with her parents in Kingsland and had a poultry unit of her own, but she was able to look after the Brook Farm stock as well, with the current small boy to help with the odd jobs and Arthur to come down from Lucton once or twice a week to keep an eye on the sheep. These were just one bunch of ewe lambs: the ewes went to the Woodhouse, Shobdon, to be tupped by one of Mr. John Owens' famous Stockley rams; and the ram lambs were parked with Sydney Price at Cressage—we were lucky in our sheep friends. This left about a hundred laying hens in fold units and many cats, who had to have bought milk as there was no cow. But the greatest wrench of all was leaving behind dog Flax and the two bitches, Fly and Flirt.

For forty years we had our own unbroken line of sheepdogs; they have always been a major part of our life. Hemp was the first—I found him while I was still teaching at M.G. At the beginning of the autumn term 1933, when I thought I was leaving for Armscote at Christmas, I searched in farming papers for sheep dog advertisements and found a litter of puppies at Hemel Hempstead, within easy distance of Gerrard's Cross. Without coherent purpose, 'just for fun', a friend and I went to see them. On an untidy poultry farm, dotted with ramshackle hen houses, we found ten or twelve small puppies in a tiny wire run—a couple of doubtful looking bitches hovered near. The pups, two litters of course, were supposed to be eight weeks old, but looked barely six—they were much too small and it seemed hopeless; but as I peered again into the pen for a last look a tiny lemon and white puppy detached himself from the rabble and bundled towards me. I picked him up and that was it—he was mine.

My idiotic suggestion to the owner that he should keep the pup for me till Christmas was turned down; so too was the idea of having him 'on approval' and bringing him back if my headmistress refused to let him stay. I paid the money demanded—maybe a couple of pounds—I forget, and risked it.

I stood on the blue carpet before Miss Chambers' desk in trepidation as I explained to her; but she was a wise woman who accepted the 'fait accompli'—she favoured my farming and I already kept my pony Polly on her Pond Meadow. After horrified exclamations about Hemp she said only that he must live on the childrens' farm and never come in the house. (She relented about this when she knew him—I stayed on an extra term and he was allowed in my room in the staff cottage!)

Meanwhile he lived among the rabbits and guinea pigs on the half of Pond Meadow not occupied by Polly and the school geese, in a roomy rabbit hutch with plenty of bedding and a wire run. I fetched him for play and lessons (Sit, Come, Good, No) in my every free period, but the distance between house, farm and cottage was at first too great for his small legs, so he rode serenely in a pale blue and pink canvas carrier bag whose colours set off the lemon and white bear cub head looking out of the top. The children loved him and were very good about not handling him—he was my dog and knew it.

When we moved to Armscote he was not so popular, as my family opposite kept cocker spaniel bitches and he was a great ladies man; but he was obedient and with me night and day, so I thought they need not have worried. At Buckley Green we were isolated and he never went off; but at Brook Farm, when quite an old dog, he came into his own. We were visiting Arthur, at work across the Hill Farm fields, when I remarked that his little sheep bitch looked in whelp— did he know what dog? 'Yes', said Arthur—'old Hemp.' I was astonished—the rascal must have left me while I was at work on Brook Farm, trotted two miles on the roads, mated the bitch, trotted straight home and I never even missed him! Arthur was full of glee. I requested and was gladly given, first pick of the litter and in due course chose a big blue dog puppy whom I called Flax.

Father and son got on well together: at night Hemp slept with me inside the caravan with Flax in a cosy, well-bedded barrel underneath. Both followed well behind a bike and Flax developed into a useful shepherd on the road; but neither showed any inclination to gather sheep in the field. They were always a help because they sat and moved to command; but the instinct to go round ('away by') was not there—we bred it into the line. People ask: 'How do you train them?' We don't—we can teach obedience, but the instinct to round up and bring the sheep has to be there.

All our dogs and bitches lived to a ripe old age except Kim, last of the line. Hemp died at fifteen, after a stroke, and then we needed a mate for Flax. I promised Mary a really well bred sheep bitch, put out some feelers and one day, while we were shearing, Mr. Howard Owens walked up the drive carrying under his arm a little black and white 'lumper', very coy and shy.

We had no idea of her breeding—we trusted Mr. Howard. We called her Fly and she worked the sheep like a champion. When the time came to mate her Mary insisted that she should go to a well-bred dog—Flax was not good enough. Arrangements were made with Mr. Charlie Morris, who had a well known worker, and at the right time Mary and Fly went off to Weston. They returned tails down—Fly thought nothing of the poor dog, but sailed straight home to accept her beloved Flax! That was the end of sending her away to mate.

Thereafter we bred and sold many puppies, keeping now and then a special bitch to continue the line. Flirt was the first of these, a sweet worker until she began to go blind with P.R.A. (progressive retinal atrophy), that one time scourge of several breeds but now almost bred out of Border Collies. We did not breed from Flirt because of this, but she was specially close to us, stayed with us all her long life and was put down on Mary's knee in the van where she always travelled.

The next bitch we kept was Bunty, a darling blue funny, who bumbled around the sheep without much idea of what she was up to; but she bred some beautiful puppies. We are lucky to have in Kingsland the celebrated trials man John James, known widely as a star in 'One Man and his Dog'. We took Bunty to his Moss, a fine dog who ran twice with the English National team. One of their puppies was our Trudy, for me the best of all. She was black, with a smooth flat coat (the only one ever), tan eyebrows, and a large white cross on her chest. Her ears were pricked and she was a brilliant worker—in the right hands she could have been a trials winner. But she will always be my special bitch—I loved her dearly.

Trudy's first whelping was a great anxiety—she was over a day and a half in labour and in the end I took her up to Kington to our splendid vet, Mr. Macleod. He laughed at her, called her a lap-dog, stood her on a table, gave her an injection and on the way home she popped out the first puppy at my feet among the gear levers. All was well after that and she produced Tess, who was perfectly marked and coated, and a true gentle shepherd without the brilliance of her mother.

We sold puppies all over the country and made through them many good friends. We flew one from Birmingham to the west of Scotland and even advertised 'Overseas delivery a speciality' on the strength of our proposed export to Marian, never to be repeated. After our visit to Tyringham we planned to send her a bitch puppy as a mate for her good dog Rufus. Meticulous arrangements were made with Great Western Railways, who guaranteed to transfer the crate from the Hereford train to the Heathrow van at Paddington and thence to the aircraft, to arrive at New York early next morning, where Bill would meet her and take her down to Tyringham. Late in the evening of despatch day a London RSPCA branch rang to tell us that the puppy was safe with them—the carefully labelled crate had been found abandoned on Paddington station. We cabled Bill—no trans-Atlantic telephone for the likes of us in those days—and the RSPCA promised to care for the puppy over the weekend, a long one for Thanksgiving—and embark her at Heathrow when they could get a flight. She arrived in New York in good condition, to be met at last by Marian and Bill, who had driven back from Tyringham. We were all so thankful to the RSPCA for a wonderful job.

As time went on we found it difficult to sell puppies—we were anxious about many of the farm homes where dogs were kept tied up: we decided to breed only for our own replacements. From Tess's last litter we kept Kim, a cheerful well-marked bitch with apparently the usual sweet temperament. She started to work but began to develop peculiar behaviour: she was quiet and happy in the house with us, but when outside she would flee blindly at the sound of a forestry lorry, or dash to the gate in a fury when walkers came up to the woods. We suspected her sight but it was not that. After a couple of anxious years she became so full of fear that she had to be coaxed from the house: in the end she refused our call and actually turned on us when we handled her—from anyone else she fled. We suspected a brain tumour—we could not let her go on. When at last the vet came to put her down he did not try to approach her but let us give her the first tranquilising injection. She suffered us, but cried, though we calmed her before the end. She was the last of our line.

Tess lived on for eighteen months, but she was too old for more puppies. She died after an operation in November 1977. There are so many dog lives within our time span, each leaving on us an indelible mark, each death a scar.

We were without a dog for the first time and the gap was great. We thought to wait till the spring, when the weather would be warmer for a small weaned puppy; but one December day we stopped to talk to John Tedstone, our good neighbour at The Brook, and noticed that his dear old bitch Floss was heavy in whelp. We asked to whom and John replied proudly: 'To John James' Mirk'. (Mirk won the English National in 1975 and was English Driving Champion in '76). We were promised first choice puppy, and on December 28th John rang to tell us that Floss had five—four bitches and a dog. We went to see them at three weeks old and first to crawl out from the straw bale nest was a bold bitch puppy with tan eyebrows. We picked her up and knew for sure that this was our Jane—we did not handle any of the others. When we left John went in for his dinner, returning afterwards to see that Floss and the pups were all right. She was there with them—she could jump in and out over the half stable door—but one puppy was missing. John looked everywhere and in the end found Jane hidden in a heap of coal in a shed by the house door: Floss had carried the strange smelling puppy as close as possible to the protection of her master.

We visited the puppies twice more before collecting Jane at eight weeks old; with her came her sister Pepper, whom we borrowed from John so that the two would feel warm and secure in our strange stable. This experiment was a great success—we all had a lot of fun, 'no howling' lessons were learnt, and when Pepper went home after about six weeks Jane was obedient to call and ready for 'Sit' and 'Stay'. Unable to offer such good puppy games, we started her with a ball and over the years this has been a boon to us. We have no sheep at Hill Farm in the winter and her twice daily boundary walk was not enough exercise. Ball catching became routine—she leaps and seldom misses—her timing is brilliant and if she were a cricketer she would field for England! The ball game is a bonus when children visit—she will play to their throwing and so break her fear of toddlers—she was chased once by a small boy and has never forgotten, but this is her only fear.

Jane came to shepherding sweetly—she is keen and wise, and what we should do without her I don't know. As I write in 1989 she is eleven years old: she never leaves us and follows our thoughts. I marvel at the intelligence potential in dogs and wonder whether, when humans are gone from earth and sea, dogs and whales will dominate more kindly.

But in 1955, before our trip to America, we dominated the lives of a dog and two bitches. They must be cared for in our absence, and we were happy when Raymond and Pamela offered to have old Flax in their home at Presteigne, while Fly and Flirt went to Mary's sister Margaret in Leintwardine, where they were exercised well despite the demands of a busy doctor's household. We were very grateful.

VIII
Our Trip To America

We sailed from Liverpool in the Empress of Australia on the evening of Friday, October 7th 1955, a dull day but quiet after the mid-week gale; but the after-effects of this soon made themselves felt. The ship's log read 'Rough sea', and we had four bad days. I wondered continually why we had come—homesickness and sea sickness together were hard to bear. Luckily we had a comfortable cabin and a kind stewardess, and the Empress of Australia, though an old ship, stood the weather fairly well; but she was small, and the public rooms were very hot. The Canadian Pacific Railway service was excellent—nothing was too much trouble.

The explorers who crossed the Atlantic unsure of another continent were brave men—even when you know that there is land ahead it seems vast and empty. We saw no ship from Formby to the mouth of the St. Laurence—a whale was reported but we did not have the luck to spot it. Seagulls followed us all the way, though they never seemed to come aboard; but we were delighted to find on the boat deck some tiny tit-like birds who appeared to live in the lifeboats. We sighted land on the seventh day out from Liverpool, and the two day voyage up the St. Laurence was glorious—hot sun, blue sky, and steep cliffs on either side, clad in firs to the water's edge, with here and there a white coastguard house apparently accessible only from the river. The day clouded as we approached Quebec, and perhaps because of this and because we had heard too much of their magnificence, we were disappointed with the famous Heights. We tied up on the messy waterfront and went ashore in the dark and wind. A half-tight French Canadian taxied us at breakneck speed to the top of the Heights, where we looked at the very pretentious pseudo-French Chateau Fontenac, a vast C.P.R. hotel, and returned thankfully to the ship. No doubt it was the wrong impression of Quebec.

The river banks between Quebec and Montreal flatten out and we sailed through dull marshy country broken with inlets and bare islands on which small herds of rough looking Friesian cattle picked for a living. There were short legged cobs in twos and threes, but not a sheep to be seen, and this we found general through the whole trip. The houses were mostly poor shacks, supposed to be white, nearly all needing paint and many in disrepair. There was an occasional small patch of ploughing, but no sign of any tidy farming.

We reached Montreal at mid-day on Saturday, October 14th. The approach to the city was interesting, and included sailing under a great bridge which seemed sure to foul our superstructure. Tying up was a work of art, as the piers were at right angles to the river and our bows ended almost in the street, to which the docks were open in places—there were people standing on the edge with nothing to stop a fall into the filthy water.

When we got ashore we found a note on our luggage to say that friends awaited us at the gates. Veronica had told Clare and Norton Fellowes of our arrival, and they had brought their car to meet us. We were whisked through the city, past the fine new hospital and up the Mountain overlooking Montreal. Near the top was a car park and no cars could go beyond. We were delighted to walk up the wooded slope and to see grey squirrels among the trees: in spite of wind and drizzle it was grand to be ashore. The view over the city and river was magnificent, and we should never have seen it but for the Fellowes. They drove us to their ultra-modern home in a pleasant suburb and we examined it thoroughly. Clare had every modern gadget and some good old furniture as well—glass bricks in the hall and wide windows everywhere let in a lot of light—we did not know

94

then how much we should miss this in the States. The house was warm but not stifling, and our visit with Veronica's friends felt like home.

We spent a comfortable night high up in the Hotel Laurentian, and breakfasted in the station restaurant, where we had an excellent meal and bought fresh sandwiches specially packed for our journey, which we thought a good effort at 7.30 a.m. on a Sunday. We embarked in brilliant sunshine on probably our best train journey—from Montreal to Troy, New York, running down the wooded western shore of Lake Champlain, with the long range of the Green Mountains behind us in the east, and the water brilliantly blue beside us. Towards noon, however, the sky clouded. We left the lake and plunged into the steady rain which we soon found had been falling for three days without a break. The land lay wetter and wetter as we ran south—what little tillage we saw stood in pools of water, with implements abandoned in mid-furrow (but it seemed common practice in America to leave everything out in the weather, including expensive motor cars.) The grass looked poor and yellow, with a few dairy cattle—Friesians mostly, with a sprinkling of Guernseys, all dehorned—standing with their backs up, and never a sheep to be seen.

Marian and Bill gave us a tremendous welcome at Troy station, and drove us, still in pouring rain, the sixty miles to Tyringham, Mass. On the way we saw wild deer, and a skunk dead on the road—that was the only time we saw either, though both are common and we smelt skunk later. We also missed seeing porcupine, which are often about chewing wooden buildings, and beaver, which abound in the Tyringham brook. We waited by their dam on several evenings at dusk, and a neighbour shot his fifteenth on permit while we were there, so we were disappointed not to see one. Beaver were protected by the State of Massachussets, but their dam building in the brook held back the water on a patch of ground the Gelsleichters were trying to reclaim, so they had a state permit to destroy them. I hoped that this would not continue indefinitely—the beaver's patient industry seems to deserve better.

Side of Craholla house

Tyringham is in the Berkshires, a country of rolling hills clothed with trees—green firs, silver birches, and maples in a blaze of scarlet and gold. Clear streams dash down the hillsides into valley brooks, along which are dotted the wooden white houses of once prosperous farms. Many of these had become summer residences, their fine tobacco drying barns turned into studios or garages, their land run back to brush; some had been even less fortunate, and all that remained was a pile of rotting boards and a gaunt stone chimney in the middle of thick woods. The few farmers left milk bare-looking Friesians—or Holsteins, as they are called—which picked about on stony patches or were tethered on unfenced fields around the homestead. Everyone had a bit of land, yet no-one thought of keeping poultry—people drove miles to buy a dozen eggs from Marian. Some farmers augmented their income by running a lumber business—wood abounded, yet was expensive to buy because the cost of labour was so great; and the same men would often tap their maple trees and make syrup which was hard to sell at a profit because corn syrup tastes nearly the same and can be made more cheaply. The maple trees are tapped in March, when the days are warm and sunny, the nights cold, and the sap rises quickly. One tree will give up to eighty gallons of sap, but this brings only a gallon of syrup, made by boiling off over a wood fire in the open. Pure maple syrup sold for about six dollars (then £2) a gallon, so its production was not a job for hired labour at a dollar and a half (53p) an hour.

The Gelsleichters had about sixty acres of land, but only thirty were cleared, and on these Marian had done a good job ploughing up and re-seeding, but was on the way to spoiling her work by taking hay each year. The land was light and sandy, and there was hardly a trace of clover left in the yellow sward. We found only one fence on the farm, of thirty inch pig wire running snake-like and unstrained to enclose the two acres on which fifty-one sheep were supposed to stay. Naturally they popped over the low wire or dived under its folds, despite the incredible collection of brushwood flung in the gaps to stop them. After the first few days, when we were called often from our job of stripping the deep litter house to collect them from the heights of the neighbouring woodland, we convinced our hosts that it would be wise to enclose the farm. The first fence was planned, and old Harry called in to help for a couple of days. Harry was a rough general workman, and looked it; but he arrived in a shining new Buick limousine which he ran as well as a station wagon, and as his wages worked out at about £4 a day, no doubt he could well afford to do so. Every workman in the States seemed to run a car, and they were nearly all large new ones. The car parks made every factory look like a crowded race meeting, and at knocking off time the traffic congestion in even a small town was becoming a major problem. The old car dumps, where last year's models were piled two or three deep on top of older wrecks, were an eye-sore all over the country, and parking in big cities was working up to a national crisis.

We were not impressed with Harry's work, which was slow and untidy, and we put up the next and longest fence by ourselves. We also made a couple of light gates, and left the whole place enclosed and gated in patches radiating from the big barn where the sheep were foddered and lay at night. They were shut in too much, but would then have been able to run out at will on five to six acres at a time, while the remainder rested. With alternate mowing and grazing and plenty of phosphates the land should improve and carry as many sheep as the barn will house — that is, about twenty-five ewes. We found over fifty cross-bred ewes of all ages, yearling ewes by a Montadale ram, and the remains of this year's lamb crop. The adult sheep looked well, but the lambs were poor and many of them runts. Marian's broken ankle had handicapped her work that summer, and we were able to help her draw and market lambs (at a shocking price) until the flock was down to thirty-five.

We had a shock when we entered the Gelsleichter house, but soon found out that it was cool compared with most. One of the three windows in our room opened, and so did a door into the garden on the opposite side, so that we slept in comfort in a through draught. We could turn off the heat, and during November our sponges were often solid with ice, and we kept fit. The rest of the house was hermetically sealed, and though we often heard American complaints that they could not sleep because it was so hot, no one ever dreamed of opening a window. They were much concerned with temperature but had little idea of the weather. Most of the homes we saw were not only stifling but stale in atmosphere, and in perpetual twilight, as all the windows were draped with muslin curtains and covered with half drawn blinds. Walls were usually covered with dark-patterned Victorian paper, and the furniture and numerous knicknacks were incredibly old-fashioned. This seemed to be the general way of living, but the standard was probably different among the more widely travelled, as our very pleasant last day with the Eldredges in Virginia seemed to show. In hotels we found modern bedrooms where we could always get the radiator off and the windows open; but in the public rooms lack of daylight prevailed, and to have breakfast on a sunny morning with all the blinds down and electric light on seemed very wrong to us. The Americans try themselves high: they live in their overheated houses wearing thin summer shirts or dresses, but dart out into freezing streets to get the car or buy a paper without extra clothing of any kind. They looked pallid and sickly, and though they did not seem to have the heavy colds one would expect, they lacked energy and had no idea of a hard day's manual work.

During our first days Marian drove us around locally: we were amused with the shopping at the A & P (Atlantic and Pacific Co.) — a chain store. The customer wheeled a high wire trolley and collected her choice of packaged food in infinite variety. There were unfamiliar vegetables—egg plant, sweet potatoes, peppers, yams, and squash (our marrow in various disguise). The meat was wrapped and priced, and the twenty-eight varieties of ice-cream were found in an ice-box and kept thus at home for days. On the way out all purchases were taken from the trolley by the cashier, checked and paid for at a turnstile, from where at the larger markets they travelled by conveyor belt to an outside wall, where a boy loaded them on to the customer's car as she drove round.

The ice-box played a great part in the American household— Marian would sell old hens, plucked but not dressed, by the half dozen to private customers who kept and ate them as required; and several people bought her lambs at seventeen dollars (£5.10) apiece regardless of weight, had them slaughtered and kept them also in the ice-box. They would be a great improvement on the 'lamb' sold in the supermarkets, which tasted like old ewe and no doubt accounted for the very low consumption in the States—a point of concern to sheep breeders which should be energetically dealt with by their propaganda people. The scope for an increased sheep population was enormous: vast tracts of land with hardly a sheep to be seen, or bunches of under twenty in fifty acre fields. Few of the pedigree cattle men run any sheep at all, though on some of the good farms we saw there was any amount of keep for a flock to follow the cattle. Labour and tradition are both to blame—the cattle man looked down on the sheep-herder in the early days.

The first pedigree Hereford herd we saw was Mr. Shuttleworth's at Sunset Lodge in Warren, Mass. Marian drove us on a bitterly cold but sunny day after a night of icy, gale-force wind and morning snow—that was October 25th. We enjoyed the run east, through Springfield, a town about the size of Hereford, with good public buildings and a fair sized railway junction, where we saw a long train-load of fat pigs bound for Chicago. The road followed the Chicopee river much of the way, and there were many signs of the disastrous floods of August 19th—huge sections of road swept away, banks shored up while traffic crept one way, an odd car grounded in mid-river and houses with one side stripped off, hanging naked over the water.

Sunset Lodge is high and steep, a real hardy farm where the cattle carried tremendous coats and looked very fit. It is a small herd of neat short-legged cows headed by a young Zato bull with a grand hind leg but a little rough over the tail. There were also three Vern Diamond heifers which had been sent to this bull, but unfortunately they were disappointing beside the American cattle. We were very glad to meet Mr. Shuttleworth, who was kindness itself, and the view he showed us from a beautiful clover ley over 1,000ft. high was superb; but unfortunately the wind was too intensely cold for us to look at the cattle as long as we wanted.

This was our first long run in America, and we were much impressed by the good standard of driving. There was none of the speeding we had expected—average speed seemed slower than in England, though this was partly due to many hold ups for flood damage. There were innumerable road signs—too many, and drivers tended to ignore them. 'Soft shoulder' was a frequent one, meaning that the tarmac ended before the road edge, a menace to dreamy drivers. We were amused at 'Thickly Settled' instead of 'Densely Populated', a relic of earlier days; and 'Falling Rock', and 'Rolling Stones' were too frequent to mean much. In cities there were far more traffic lights than we had, and everyone drove on their brakes, so that the streets sounded alarming but were really quite safe. Private car owners seemed to have little mechanical sense and abused their expensive vehicles unmercifully. The wear and tear which this must have caused was watched by state law: every six months brakes, windscreen wiper and headlamp alignment had to be checked by an approved garage, which then stamped the windscreen with an O.K. chit. The theory was better than the practice we saw: when the car was stationary the lamp alignment check on a marked screen was good, but the hand brake was tested on the flat and the foot brake not at all!

Car parking on the street was universal, and lights were not required; few city dwellers owned a garage, and their cars lived in the road beneath their windows—in New York City they had to be moved daily from side to side. It was strange to see thousand dollar limousines covered in inches of snow, with icicles hanging from their bumpers; but they always seemed to start when needed.

On October 20th 'hunting' started in Massachusetts. At 7.30 a.m. we were awakened by a couple of men with guns and a beagle, who asked permission to walk over the Gelsleichter land. Their courtesy was unusual, as any land that was not 'posted'—that is, marked with 'No hunting' signs—could be shot over. The game—chiefly pheasants and rabbits—was the property of the state, and the number that may be taken in any one day was strictly limited, returning cars being liable to check by the game warden. The season, too, was short, and varied from state to state—in Massachusetts it was between October 20th and November 26th, and the deer season was one week only from November 28th. Hunters had to wear red shirts—these were warm woollen jackets, usually in scarlet and black checks, very comfortable—and red caps, bearing their gun licence number like a car registration plate! Hunting probably accounted for the number of privately owned dogs of hound type, mostly beagles, though we saw a basset hound in New York City, where every other person has a dog, and the side walks are filthy. The Americans are strange with animals—sentimental and not very clever with their dogs, given to keeping strange pets—we heard of a cat in a cage, and single sheep kept in the house by ordinary working people; but the handling of stock at the local auction, where we took a bunch of Marian's lambs, was deplorable. Lorries were either overcrowded, or with single beasts slipping about on unlittered floors open to the weather. In the pens the overcrowding was dreadful, young calves being wedged like sardines, though there were empty pens next door; and every time an animal was moved it was battered unmercifully. Gertrude, who ran a store near Marian's, came with us and was astonished and angry, so perhaps there was no public awareness to check such behaviour. We wrote a letter to the local paper and hope it may have done some good.

In early November we spent a couple of nights in New York City. We drove down the west side of the Hudson river, starting in the very early morning and dropping Bill at the Bendix Aviation Company's works in New Jersey. These were in vast factory filled mud-flats, whence traffic converged into eight lines to cross the amazing George Washington suspension bridge, then said to be the longest single span bridge in the world. Like many new bridges and thruways in the States, it was being paid for by heavy tolls. Unfortunately the days we spent in New York were three of autumn's best, with warm sun and cloudless sky, too good for town.

Much of the city was filthy, the side-walks disgusting, and seemingly endless garbage collection went on in mid-street—the trucks could not pull into the kerb because of the unbroken lines of parked cars, so that open dustbins were carried shoulder high through pedestrians and tipped on to rising conveyor belts in the lorries. Parts of course were more pleasant and next day Marian's niece Gloria came to conduct us round.

We went to the Empire State Building and took the elevator on its first stage up to the eighteenth floor—this took four minutes. You changed lifts, travelled up another twelve, and went out on to a circular open balcony below which lay the view of the city which kept the Queen Mother up there so long. It is breath-taking—those vast buildings dwarfed like a tiny model, with cars crawling like bright coloured toys in the slit-like streets, and the network of water and islands, houses and chimneys spread out like a map for miles

On the New York Harbour Ferry

around. We saw the Queen Mary tied up in the docks, with the Britannic lying beside her like a rowing boat. I felt homesick and wished we could sail this trip instead of next.

We did not see enough of the Rockefeller Centre, 'a city within a city', containing the famous Radio City Music Hall, and fountains, statues, and an open air ice rink where we could have spent hours watching the gay skaters — there was one girl whose movements were really lovely, and the children were fun. However, we had to meet Marian at her mother's for tea, which was served in glass cups, and later join Bill at a weird and gloomy Italian restaurant where we dined before the theatre. They took us to 'Bus Stop' — a disappointment, as we had expected to see 'Cat on a Hot Tin Roof' — and as Kim Stanley was off sick and the leading man had died the week before, we were unlucky in our first experience of the theatre on

Broadway. The play was fair, but not good enough to withstand such vicissitudes.

We left for Tyringham as early the next morning as we could.

We drove back on the parkway east of the river, one of the many such roads which run for hundreds of miles in neat beauty through the countryside. They were a great improvement on the hoarding-plastered main roads which in many parts link one city with the next in an endless line of jerry-built shacks and 'diners'; but they were so well kept that they seemed artificial—hundreds of miles of broad gang-mown grass verges bordering neat woodland, but hardly a bit of honest farming to be seen.

We ate our sandwiches beside a lovely lake, and stopped the car again to photograph two enormous stinking Mountain billy goats tethered in a smallholding—where nannies to suit such monstrosities could come from heaven knows! The sun was still glorious and we were thankful to reach Tyringham, where we had a grand welcome from Gertrude and Rufus, who had held the fort together in our absence. Rufus jumped up madly, a bad habit which at Marian's request we did our best to check while we were there; but he was a grand dog and in time would make a splendid shepherd.

One of our oddest expeditions was to the Inter-College football match between Union and Williamstown. Bill is an old Union man and was very excited, especially when Union won! We started from home about an hour late; for the first and only time during our stay Bill took the wheel and we wandered weaving along roads with many near misses for two-thirds of the way until they realised how late we were, when Marian slapped us along the last third at speed. We arrived on the campus at Williamstown just as the game began.

This American football is an astonishing game. The players are heavily padded on shoulders, knees and chest, and wear crash helmets, but despite such elaborate protection there were innumerable casualties during this game—though fewer than at a professional match we saw afterwards on television. The sides toss for first kick, and the small size rugby ball is punted into the opponents' hands.

The holder is immediately set on by markers who are also charged by their markers, but he must try to make a yard or two before being brought down. The game proceeds endlessly like this, no one able to run more than a step or two, the gains being measured in yards by the many linesmen. There are constant huddles for consultation or coaching, and if ten yards are not gained after four tries the ball must be punted as far as possible down the opponents' end and they start the whole affair again. The intricacies of the game were, of course, lost on me, and I have probably described it inaccurately; but the effect on an untutored spectator was unbearably slow, and would surely drive a rugby player mad with impatience. Far more amusing were the antics of the cheer leaders, who performed extraordinary gymnastics in front of their section of the spectators, and incited them to varied chants in support of their side. Young men and girls wandered hand in hand on the touch line during play, many of them looking untidy and dirty. The girls nearly all wore sloppy jeans and filthy white gym shoes or shabby flat-heeled dancing sandals, but their top halves were often resplendent with jewellery and make-up. Also on the side line was a young man with a cable in hand with which he operated the huge electric scoreboard at one end of the field. At half-time a party of the college Air Force Cadets gave a deplorable marching display—their carriage, turn-out and performance were equally poor. Some sort of half-time diversion seems general at these matches—there was some good army marching at the television game.

We dined that night at the Williams Inn, an extensively advertised country hotel, white and pleasant outside but too much cluttered within—again the heavy Victorian wallpapers and knicknacks. Before the very good dinner, which was served from 5.30 p.m. onwards, we drove round the fine dark-red brick college buildings and on for a few miles into the State of Vermont, up a trippery sort of road which did not give us the proper feeling of the rugged mountain country—it was just one more state to add to our list.

On November 7th we visited a pedigree Corriedale flock near Sheffield, about ten miles from Tyringham. We made a late start, and did not get there until 4 p.m.; however, the sheep were nearly all indoors in a dimly-lighted barn, most of it below ground level. They were grossly overcrowded—there were about seventy indifferent ewes in one lot, shut in with a good stock ram—and some of the ewe lambs especially looked sick or unthrifty. Mrs. Lund, a rough hard-working lady, was very pleasant, but inclined to lecture—she had not been at pedigree sheep breeding long and the people with least experience always have most to say. We began to think that untidiness was typical of American farming.

After this, our visit to Powisset next day was indeed a joy. In 1953 Miss Amelia Peabody made the largest import of Herefords into the States for many years, and we were very keen to see her herd. We managed to start at 9.30 a.m., and with only half an hour for lunch reached Dover, Mass. punctually at 2.15—quite an achievement! We called at his house for Miss Peabody's manager, Mr. Wilcox—we liked him and his wife immensely, and were soon talking of mutual friends. They had stayed in Hereford during their buying tour—poor Mrs. Wilcox was laid low with 'flu at the Green Dragon Hotel—he of course had been around all the herds. It was great fun to hear their impressions.

The farm buildings, a few yards on up the road, were about the best kept we had ever seen—every tool clean and hung in place, boxes and yards white-washed, doors painted, and the condition of the cattle and their licked clean mangers showed that the tidiness was not all on the surface. Like so many American barns this was built on two levels, with lines of boxes above and cattle yards under, approached by a gently winding ramp.

We saw first a bunch of three American-bred show heifers, well grown and fleshed. The best bodied was to be retained and the other two sold. We commented on the nice head of one of these last, but Mr. Wilcox said that they were culling all cattle with dished faces and broad muzzles as they seemed more likely to breed dwarfs than

106

longer headed cows. This bogey of dwarfism haunted American Hereford breeders, and was of course the reason for the current increase in imports from Britain.

In the next box was a young bull by Atok Uranus out of a Wetmore Oyster cow. He had lots of bone and a good back end, but was weak behind the shoulder. Next door to him was a really lovely yearling heifer by Uranus from Chadshunt Fern, who was doing very well for Powissett.

We went from the range of boxes through a fine tarmac open yard to the most beautiful patch of green rye on which Uranus and his cows—about thirty—made a grand picture. The old bull detached himself and came striding homewards for a feed, so that we were able to handle him well. He was in really good store condition and moved beautifully. He was not, I think, a particularly big bull by our standards, but his size was a legend out there, which indicated how small American cattle tended to be. He was very neat, level and deep, but perhaps a shade too long in the middle. They were very proud of him at Powissett, and the really good calves he was getting fully justified their pride.

With him were many good cows, but the English bred ones were outstanding, though they carried noticeably less coat than the native cattle, even when they had been several years in America. We saw Leen Mother, a grand bodied cow by Atok Punch, Wenlock Tiptoe, Chadshunt Fern and Leen Gillian, who made top price at Regina that summer. Back in the building later we saw perhaps the nicest thing on the place—a heifer calf by Chadshunt Joe out of a Hillcrest cow—the Hillcrest herd, now dispersed, must have been one of the finest in America.

Mr. Wilcox was tremendously interested in the cattle and the farming and we were delighted to be with him—even his American accent was a pleasant one. The farm was about a hundred acres of cleared ground, with more being steadily added from the many hundreds of woodland which Miss Peabody owned in the district. We had wondered while working at Tyringham whether it was economically possible to reclaim and get a living from this very poor New England land—obviously so many people have tried, run it out, and moved west. Powissett proved that very fine crops can be grown and a beautiful farm made by someone with the money and the will to keep improving the land; but it was very doubtful whether someone with no outside resources could make much of a living. The regular farm equipment only was used for reclamation, and with this it took about five years to get a wood into full production—the time could have been much shortened, of course, by the use of bulldozers, crawlers, and so on. Miss Peabody had a fine herd of Hampshire pigs, surely our Large Whites, the breeding stock running out, and the litters and feeding pigs in a fine Danish house—and she was putting up a new range of bull boxes with silo, barn and outside yards. She must have been a wonderful person—her manager spoke of her with warm affection. We were sorry to miss her, but she was busy with Red Cross duties in Boston, where she had a large town house. Her house at Dover was unpretentious, set in the middle of woods through which Mr. Wilcox drove us. There were two small lakes in which the estate people could fish, and a studio near the stables—Miss Peabody was also a sculptor.

The stables were not under Mr. Wilcox's management, but he spoke of the horses with great enthusiasm, and when we expressed interest rang the head horseman to say that we were coming. We drove into a circular stable yard, with an old apple tree on clipped grass in the centre and white and green painted buildings around. Inside, about a dozen loose boxes faced each other across a paved alley-way; they were bright with new paint, black below, red on the bars above. It was knocking off time, and the horses were done up for the night, spotless, the youngsters bedded with straw, the rest with peat moss, but all littered well up the walls in the good old way. We were a bit puzzled about the horses—they were described as thoroughbreds, and a horse of Miss Peabody's breeding was winning races in America, but they were not quite in the same class as the English thoroughbred, smaller, stockier, and shorter in the neck. We also saw the beautifully kept tack room, with gleaming bridle cases, every kind of saddle including a Western, and a mass of huge rosettes. In another harness room we found a shy little Border Collie bitch, a good one. Dick, the head horseman, breeds them, and we were sorry that he was away on holiday, so that we had no details of his dogs.

Near the stables were some good sheep pens, with hard runs. The Hampshire stock rams were in them, and though they did not claim to be show sheep they were very useful and well grown indeed, according to American standards. We did not see the ewes, as it was then dusk, but it was nice to find a few sheep on a pedigree cattle farm—a very rare thing, it seems.

We were given a delicious 'American tea', as Mr. Wilcox had described it in his invitation. This turned out to be coffee and home-made date bread and butter—awfully good—and we did enjoy the chat with the Wilcoxes. We made the long drive back in good form after our best farm visit yet.

A few days after this we struck out from Tyringham on our journeying alone. We bused plesantly from Pittsfield to Albany, N.Y., and thence took train for Buffalo and Niagara Falls.

We travelled over four thousand miles by train in the States, and if only the coaches and waiting rooms were not so abominably overheated, very pleasant would it have been. On some trains it was an endurance test to sit in them, and sometimes the Americans found it so too, but no one thought of regulating the fan, and of course none of the windows were made to open. The seats were two by two, like a bus, very comfortable, with foot rests and high adjustable backs, so that you felt fairly private. Most of the engines were diesel or electric, and the running was very smooth, though seldom on time. There were dining cars on all long distance trains, but the food was very expensive, and we found it best to provide ourselves with sandwiches (easily bought and always good) or buy from the men who carried a basket up and down the train. There was iced water, with paper cups, available in every coach—a great boon; and sometimes we bought milk in half-pint cartons, with straws, from the basket man. The coaches were usually light painted inside with often a good picture, the artist named, on the end wall; and great care was taken to keep the floor clean (but not the windows) sweepers coming on board from time to time. The dirty windows may be explained by the fact that no American ever looked out of them—Venetian blinds were provided, and nearly always used—the brighter the winter sun, the more firmly was it shut out. When we protested that we were travelling to see the country, people gave way at once, but with surprise—it was definitely odd. (By the way, we were variously mistaken for Canadians—several times—Swedes, and Germans.)

The 'conductors' or train men amused us a lot. There was almost one a coach who examined tickets after each stop, often issuing new ones, which looked like making work. Each had several coats on hangers near his seat, and on wet days an umbrella was produced when he dismounted at the small stations and placed a stool for his passengers to descend on to the line. There were few places with platforms, and people wandered across the track when their train came in; neither were there gates at even the busiest level crossing—sometimes a boom, and always a traffic light, and the trains hooted loudly as they approached; but it seemed dangerous to us.

The goods trains were interesting—enormously long and heavy, often with two engines, their trucks twice the size of ours and emblazoned with enchanting labels, such as 'Santa Fé, all the way', 'The Route of the Zephyrs', 'Be specific, ship Union Pacific', and many more. We got a great kick out of them.

The large station waiting halls were enormous and stifling. Many of them have huge, fine murals; at Buffalo there was an enormous bronze statue of the beast, at Montreal a beautiful model of the old 'Empress of Britain'. Within the waiting halls was every conceivable service, huge information bureaux, refreshment rooms, and the Travellers' Aid Association office, which we found most useful. Passengers assembled for their train at one of the many entrances leading to the numbered tracks, but were not admitted until the train arrived. Then they need only hurry through the bit of fresh air they dislike so much, but this method was very slow, and perhaps accounted for the persistent and expected late running.

We reached Niagara Falls, a considerable city, in the evening, and thanks to a chance tip took ourselves by bus across the river and through customs to the Canadian side, where we found the very comfortable Sheraton-Brock Hotel. It was a mistake to see the Falls first by night: a tawdry blue light was playing on the water, which looked hemmed in by the city. We went to bed disappointed, but next morning things were different. The Sheraton-Brock dining room is on the top floor, and two walls of it are windows, overlooking the Falls. It was a wonderful experience to breakfast in view of that mass of boiling water, the American Falls straight in front, the Canadian Horseshoe to the right, falling eternally to the angry river which for ever returns its clouds of spray.

We walked steadily all day: first sheer down to a stony beach where some boats are tied, and seabirds ride on the choppy water—you could climb out on to rocks and feel almost on an island, but always you had to shut out the sight of the city behind the Falls. Back up again to the cliff top, where we spent the two-minute silence, still observed at their Memorial on November 11th by our Canadian friends, facing the water with memorable thoughts. Then we walked upstream, on a wet promenade high above the river, to the pavilion where you embark for 'Under the Falls'. We spent some time outside it, leaning over the rails and watching the incredible mass of water roaring by. We were glad that it was winter, with few people about. Then we paid our dollar, were fitted up with oilskins and gumboots by stout ladies who were proud to tell us that they had also fitted up the Queen, and descended in an elevator to the tunnel behind the Falls. This is hewn through the rock, many yards inside, with here and there galleries running to observation points directly behind the wall of water, crashing past eternally to the pool below. We stayed down a long time, almost alone, and felt small in the face of such power.

We returned to our starting point, crossed the river by the new Rainbow Bridge, a fine joint construction by Canada and the United States, and went through gardens to the edge of the American Falls, where the river races past like an express train and disappears suddenly a few yards from where you stand. It was an amazing sensation. A small bridge crossed an arm of the river a bit further upstream, and as we walked across, three wild duck rose from a quiet pool right in the middle of streaming rapids where nothing seemed able to live. Goat Island was quiet, full of trees among which wandered a mass of cock pheasants, obviously imported—but only cocks? The road ran close to the water right round the island, with made-up promontories here and there which gave a sense of being on top of the torrent racing for the Horseshoe. It was dusk by now and we should have liked longer on Goat Island; but we must have walked ten miles that day. The Americans were working hard to improve Goat Island— new paths and observation points were being made and it seems as if they, and the Canadians too, have woken almost too late and realised the enormous natural asset which they have so nearly spoiled by the ugly city on its brink. The power of the water was so tremendous that by day it was possible to shut out the buildings and feel in a natural world; but by night it was not so easy, and the playing of coloured lights on the Falls seemed all wrong. The white light only, which we saw as we crossed back to the hotel, was natural and lovely, and we did not look at the Falls again that night.

Next day we set off into the blue. No mail had come for us to Niagara, so that we did not know whether we should get to any Hereford herds or not, but we took the train for Cleveland, Ohio, hoping for the best. It was rather a dull journey, running along the shore of Lake Erie, but there were few sights of the lake—only hideous industrial plants on its edge. The country was more cultivated than any we had yet seen, but short of stock—there were acres of tomatoes and vineyards, but no sign of mechanical pickers—if all these grapes were really harvested by hand the cost must have been tremendous.

We reached Cleveland, yet another dirty noisy city, on Saturday evening, and rang the manager of McCormick Farms, Medina, from our hotel. He at once invited us to come out on Sunday morning, and we travelled the thirty miles by bus. Mr. Davis drove us on to the farm, which comprised four sets of buildings along a road running through the middle of the thousand acres. Here we learnt more of American general farming methods than anywhere else, and found the finest herd of Herefords that we had ever seen. Their show cattle were all away—a large team, they had just been first in groups of ten at the Royal at Kansas City; yet we saw beast after beast that could have been in the money at any English show. On the whole they were smaller than our average, very short in the leg but very deep. Heads were uniformly good, but often marred by a black nose which was not in the least disliked by American judges. We saw a beautiful lot of baby calves, with one or two smashers, and some good young bulls, all very well done (there were a number of Friesian nurse cows) but with large exercise paddocks. Only three stock bulls were in use on the four hundred cows, but all the breeding was done artificially by the resident vet. And what bulls they were! Hillcrest Larry Domino 12th was eleven years old, but as neat and tidy as a yearling, and very active; his getting had made a great mark—he is advertised as the 'Man 0'War of the Breed' and referred to always as 'The 12th'. He was himself International Champion, and had sired six champions and the world's record priced bull. It was good to see an old show bull looking so fit—a tribute to McCormick management. His son, a three year old, Perfect Zato Mixer, was still in show form—or so it seemed to us, though we were assured he had lost a lot of flesh; but he looked in tremendous form and would have puzzled judges at home, for you could hardly fault him in the middle, but he had an awful black nose and lots of black hair in the tail. The bulls lived in quarters of their own—beautiful boxes opening out on to separate paddocks—and seemed to be in the sole charge of the young vet, 'Doc' Fleming, who had his super laboratory in the same building. An in-calf heifer lived in the fourth box as a teaser, so everything was

113

on the spot. The 'doc' even fed his own cats in there—it was all most cosy! He was a very shy young man, but when we got him going we had a valuable half hour. We saw a very expert bandaging of Zato Mixer's foot, which had a nasty bit of foul; and we were told much about tests and veterinary practice in the States.

On the holding there was a large implement shed with a lot of good equipment tidily housed— *most* unusual in America. We saw an ordinary crop sprayer which was also used regularly to spray cattle with DDT—and we also got to the bottom of corn harvesting, which had puzzled us as we travelled. This was mid-November, and everywhere we saw fields of standing corn (that is maize—the Americans spoke of grain when they want a collective word for cereals—corn always meant maize). November is the harvesting month as the corn needs a frost or two for best maturing—the problem is to wait for this but to get the corn before snow comes. The cob grows about half way up the straw and the harvester ran down the drill stripping the cobs with a V shaped arrangement at the bottom of a narrow conveyor belt which loaded it on to a trailer behind. The straw was left standing, somewhat battered, but it was not easy to tell from a distance whether the corn has been harvested or not. Stock was then run over it—usually pigs in herds of hundreds together, pigs of all sizes and colours, many 'belties', as they called their saddlebacks, and many spots, gingers, and mixtures of these. All seemed to us grossly fat, with enormous shoulders; and where there were suckling sows there never seemed many followers. At Medina, however, there were only cattle, and these were turned straight in to glean and tread the straw, which is then disced in. Wheat follows, and we were amazed to hear that they regularly harvested 80 bushels to the acre; but they could not grow oats as well as we. We saw several samples in different places, and all were thin. Quite a lot of corn was cut for silage in the summer on these big cattle farms, and much that was harvested in autumn was electrically dried in silos and fed in a home-ground ration. We saw at McCormicks' a simple unloading device which was completely new to us: all their trailers had been fitted with a moving bed, much like a strong binder canvas, run by a portable little engine, which wound canvas plus load off the rear of the trailer.

We spent the morning with Mr. Davis around the McCormick farms, missed our bus back to Cleveland and were invited to spend the rest of the day with the Davises. We accepted thankfully, having dreaded the idea of half a Sunday in the city, and we thoroughly enjoyed being treated as part of a typical American farming family. We had a grand dinner — tea-bags served specially for us — and afterwards the eldest daughter, aged about thirteen, gave us a 'Western' trick riding display on a good little entire pony, who suffered the tail climbing, side to side jumping and other antics of his rider in a wonderful way. We were taken by the two younger girls to see the colts they have bred by him out of a little pony mare — they described all the ponies as Shetlands, but they were larger than pure Shetlands, several were piebald and they were pretty rough. The little girls had won lots of prizes with them, but they were not our show ring type at all — grand pets, though, and we thoroughly enjoyed the homely chatter, and had to answer many questions about our voyage, riding clothes in England, and the Royal Family — the girls were much older for their years than English children. We then joined their dad in watching a televised football match — an important professional game, very interesting to us after our Williamstown experience, but still dreadfully slow, and we could not compete with Mr. Davis's excitement. We ended up in Mr. McCormick's palatial farm office (bath and bedroom attached, so that he can pop out from the city when he likes) signed the visitors' book next to a top baseball player (Mr. Davis was delighted about this), and were amused at the present his office staff had lately given him — a gaily-painted waggon wheel with a musical box fitted in the hub which played when the wheel was turned. Waggons, wheels, and even old carriages were fashionable in America — several people have them as ornaments in the front garden — a remembrance perhaps of the early settlers and their laborious journeys.

We left Medina in the evening, so content after our lovely day that even the discomfort of the bus journey back to Cleveland did not daunt us. We stood all the way, packed like sardines, windows shut, heat on, and the temperature in the street over 70°. Even the Americans found it hot.

Next day we trained on west to Indianapolis. We followed all our journeys on a map, and as time went on it became obvious that we could not possibly arrive on schedule. At last the reason dawned — the train left Cleveland on Eastern Standard time, but arrived in Indianapolis on Central time — we lost an hour en route. This was easy to grasp once it dawned; but less so was the fact that there was an hour difference between the station and the street — very difficult for train catching!

However, we managed to tell Mr. Herchell Kilgore what time we should arrive at Lafayette in the morning, and he and Mrs. Kilgore were at the station to drive us out to Shadeland, the home of Vern Dermot and Vern Dorian, and one of the oldest pedigree herds in

Mr. Kilgore with Vern Dermot at Shadeland

116

America. As we drove in summer-like sunshine up to the farm we found the herdsman in a paddock by the road, attending to a newly dropped pure English calf—Dermot's third in America, out of a Curly heifer by Vern Boxer. It was a grand bull calf and the Kilgores were delighted—they reckon Dermot's first bull calf, which we saw later, would be a record breaker—it was grand to find them so enthusiastic about English cattle. Mr. Kilgore had set himself ruthlessly to stamp out dwarfism in his herd. Out of his 700 cows he had selected 80 with no trace of the tendency on either side of the pedigree, and these were to be bred to English bulls; the rest were to be run as a commercial herd only, and a very fine one it looked. The cattle at Shadeland seemed to have more scale than we had yet seen, and there were some lovely old cows—one of eleven, with a good bull calf by Dermot, was a picture; but the nicest thing we saw were three yearling heifers by Dorian, who was getting beautiful females. Shadeland seemed set fair by its imports from the Vern.

As we drove around the cattle we saw much of the 2,300 acre farm, though not the river meadows—the Wabash runs through the ground—as they were too wet for the car. Near the homestead were pleasant coppices and undulating paddocks, which might easily have been in England; but the tillage was in vast stretches—some of the corn drills were over 1 mile long! How the work was managed so well was hard to see, for there were only four men; one of these was the herdsman, and the cattle were very well done. Obviously the boss was not idle! There were no refinements, of course, and one great labour saver was interesting: many of the round hay bales were never picked up. The cattle were turned in to them when fodder was needed, and picked them over all winter, scraping down to them in the snow if necessary. None of the cows were under cover nor was anything hauled to them. Hay wasted was more than offset by labour saved, and Mr. Kilgore said that the ground was hardly ever marked—in any case there was much temporary grass, the rotation being corn (that is maize) twice, soya beans, wheat or oats, and a 3 or 4 year ley—the subsoil is gravel. There were hundreds of pigs, pedigree 'Belties', running all over the place, fat as butter. Mr. Kilgore sent between three and four thousand a year to Chicago slaughter houses.

We finished as usual in the farm office, and were immensely interested in two wonderful old prints of famous Shadeland cattle in the early days—the herd was founded in 1880. (On our return we visited Mr. Geoffrey Thomas, late of Coxall, and found at his home similar prints, in one of which was a famous Shadeland stock bull, Grove the 3rd.)

We were looking at copies of the Hereford Times—most homely in central America—and admiring the achievements of Dermot's progeny at the '55 Royal, when we found in mid-page a photograph of a winning Kerry Hill ram with our name below! We felt that our identity was indeed established—we had rung Mr. Kilgore out of the blue, with no introduction—and he was delighted. We had to sign the paper, describe the sheep, and receive our host's assurance that if ever he had any they'd be Kerries.

Sheep were now the topic and we were next driven to Purdue University, where Mr. and Mrs. Kilgore met as students. Here *at last* we saw some good sheep! It was the week before the International Show at Chicago, and the head shepherd, Tom Means, who had brought out many champions, had two pens each of Hampshire, Shropshire, and Southdown wether lambs. They were all tidy, and beautifully turned out—both Hampshires and Shropshires were smaller than ours, and the latter very woolly-faced—but the Southdowns were grand, and we heard since that one of them was Supreme Champion. We did enjoy some real sheep talk again, comparing trimming methods—they all 'fit' theirs on a table with a little stock and neck strap. Tom too was an ex-student of Purdue; these American universities were wonderfully complete, each with an important and comprehensive agricultural unit right on the campus. We were due to catch a train, and did not have long enough at Purdue, but were able to walk through some of the magnificent halls and library, and to get an idea of the lay-out—twenty or thirty fine buildings, and more in the making, grouped around the grass of the campus. We would have liked much more time there, but our longest train journey was due to begin. We travelled overnight, from Lafayette, Indiana, to Tyringham, Mass.—nearly a thousand miles, never more than fifteen minutes between connections, train or bus, but what a short distance it looks on the map!

We were glad to settle down again at Tyringham, now a second home to us. We had a big job on hand—the pig wire and steel stakes had come, and we embarked on ten days' steady work, fencing in the farm. We did it by ourselves, using the tiny Massey-Harris Cub tractor to strain the wire—not very good, as she reared up if you pulled more than fifty yards at a stretch. Some of the wire we had to set on top of an old wall made of stone which surely was hauled laboriously off the ground by tobacco planters long ago—we felt like the Pilgrim Fathers, building it up again. We made a couple of light sheep gates and cut and set many strong posts and stays—not a long job in the sandy Craholla soil—you could get down 4ft. in about fifteen minutes. We drove home the last staple at dusk the day before our departure for Virginia, leaving the whole farm enclosed and safe for sheep.

During this last stretch at Tyringham we had one grand expo.—to the University of Connecticut.at Storrs. Here we spent three hours with Professor Hale, who was in charge of the agricultural department—a great privilege, which we valued highly and shall always remember. Storrs ran two small beef herds—Hereford and Angus—it was interesting to see the two breeds side by side in the same conditions.

A good deal of grass silage was made, and self-feeding, for cattle and sheep, was being tried. The stack for the sheep was on a concrete yard where they ran from an open building—but it looked as if the silage was too solid for the sheep to bother much with unless they were starving. These good yards also housed bull calves and the stock bull, again Hillcrest Larry breeding, and there we saw a grand gadget, of which Mary took a photograph: an electrically operated

119

Electrically lifted cattle sling, Storrs University

cattle slings. The beast was led alongside a vertical table, webbing straps were fastened under him, and the table slowly and quietly tipped him off his feet, carrying him right up to the horizontal if necessary. It was used for horses as well as cattle, and we thought it one of the best gadgets we had ever seen.

There were two breeds of sheep at Storrs: a nice little flock of Southdown ewes, headed by a good ram lamb who certainly looked very well worth his cost of $150 (£50); and some small woolly-faced Shropshires.

On our way to Storrs that morning we had called to look at a Shropshire flock belonging to a Mr. La Vieri, who had lately imported a ram from Mr. Gibson Whittles in an effort to get more size and cleaner faces. To our disappointment this ram was away in Indiana; but both here and at Storrs the Shropshires were far too small, and the wool on their faces was enough to cause total blindness if not trimmed off. The Storrs people want another breed and were most interested in our Kerries.

Unorthodox shearing ideas interested us—Professor Hale spoke of shearing some ewes in September because they were going away to a ram and he wanted to bring them on quickly; and of shearing a month before lambing to keep the ewes clean and to make them bring their lambs back into the warm building. We had quite a discussion here, as we were not very keen. Scour was a trouble at Storrs, although the sheep were a good deal on concrete—no injections were given as routine, but PTZ (Phenothiazine) in mineral salt was kept continuously in front of them. We were a long time in the sheep barn, talking of this and that.

We saw some interesting ideas in the implement sheds, including good aluminium pig gates, portable cattle scales, and a portable sheep bath which was in regular service around the state at 15 cents (5p.) a sheep dipped. But the best tool of all was at work: all the afternoon it travelled to and fro—a modern muck spreader drawn by two beautiful Percheron mares, imported from Messrs. Chivers' stud at Cambridge. They were a grand sight, and in charge of their good old waggoner they did a lot of work while we were there. They came into the fine horse stable at dusk, as we were looking at the University stud of Morgan horses—a breed named after a Civil War soldier, when no doubt they were used as troop horses. They surely derive from our Welsh cob, though the Arabian influence is more apparent. We saw their two stallions and many mares, the majority liver chestnut, with a few bays and browns. The students could take a riding course, and were also taught driving and the care of tack.

We finished up in the dairy, and saw Guernsey, Jersey, Friesian and Ayrshire cows tied up for milking—milk was collected in bulk, and the cow pen was right by the road so that the pipes ran straight from cows to cooler to tanker standing outside.

It was dark when we left the agricultural side of Storrs, but Professor Hale drove us right through the middle of the university buildings to give us an idea of their size and scope. As we were leaving he took us into the cattle lecture hall, and this was the most impressive sight of all—a huge building, 160 ft. long and 54 ft. wide, with tiers of seats around a big peat moss ring, used solely for cattle demonstrations and lectures. A collection of the horns of all breeds decorated the front of the gallery. The place was warm and beautifully appointed, but unostentatious—it was, in fact, a practical show ring, typical of the way in which things are done at Storrs. We left feeling much impressed and deeply grateful to Professor Hale for the time he had given to us.

That was our last outing from Tyringham. On the evening the fence was finished we packed our bags, and leaving most of them for the kind Marian to bring to New York by car, we set off by train for the last week-end in Washington and Virginia. We had grown little roots in Tyringham and it hurt to pull them up. Marian and Bill saw us off from Lee station by a very early train, and we shall always have a picture of those two small figures in duffle coats and berets, waving us off. We saw them again in New York, of course, but it is the country goodbye that we shall remember best.

The line from Lee to New York follows water much of the way, and was out of action in the floods. Travel on it was still very slow—indeed we were held up for an hour by a derailment—and the damage still to be seen was incredible. 'Washed-out' they call it—roads, railway lines, houses and gardens just swept away down the narrow valleys—the repair work going on was colossal and the cost to the country must have been staggering.

We were hours late in New York, but there was a train to Washington every hour, so that did not matter. We decided to cross New York to the Pennsylvania station by subway, to compare it with our underground. This involved a change from the shuttle train, which goes endlessly to and fro across the city, to the ordinary subway which goes up and down. All was quite simple, but we were at the end of the queue for one train. I stepped on, the doors shut, and Mary was left standing on the platform! I had all them money and we had no address in New York. However, we joined up safely by the next train and have laughed a lot about it since; but at the time it was a horrid moment.

Percheron horses to a muck spreader, Storrs University

We reached Washington at dusk and walked it by moon and floodlight, and very lovely it looked—the only city we saw which seemed to us individual and gracious. There are wide open spaces, squares with large trees, acres of grass around the tall George Washington Memorial, and in front of The White House and the many other palatial Government buildings. The streets are wide, not overshadowed by skyscrapers, the railway station approach is magnificent and altogether there is a sense of dignity very fitting in the capital of that mighty country.

We travelled on through Virginia by bus, and very pleasant this was for a change. Our first stop was Staunton, advertised as 'The Queen City of the Shenandoah Valley', but as it is a small country town not much bigger than Leominster this seems rather a grand title! It is the birthplace of Woodrow Wilson, and the scene of some of the toughest fighting in the Civil War—Gettysburg is quite near. We stayed at the Stonewall Jackson, an old-fashioned but very comfortable hotel, with better food than we had met so far. The whole way of living in the South is more leisured and carefree than the

North, and the Virginian countryside seemed much more like home to us. There were pleasant houses, many stone built, surrounded by white-railed paddocks, with frequent pedigree herd signs at the road gates. We saw several stud farms, too, with thoroughbred mares grazing in park-like meadows—very different from the poor grass fields of New England and the corn land of the mid-West.

We had come to Virginia to see pedigree sheep and our first visit was to Mr. Dave Canning's Suffolks at Sugar Loaf, Staunton. Mr. Canning was at the Chicago Exposition (where we heard later that he bought the Suffolk Champion), but his secretary met us in town and drove us the four miles out to Sugar Loaf. The young farm manager and his very young daughter took us round the sheep—a large flock of good well-grown Suffolks on a grand sheep farm—lots of banks but not much shelter, though the very nice ewe lambs were in the shade of a wood. Mr. Canning is a master of the advertising art, and we knew his stock rams, Poweram and Lampblack, by heart before we went. We expected from the build-up to see something really smashing—we found just two good Suffolk rams. Probably an animal so much advertised should be kept in near show condition to meet his visitors—no doubt a Suffolk expert would have found good points that we missed, but they were not outstanding sheep and their store condition did not help.

Preparations for a reduction sale were going on at Sugar Loaf—a professional 'fitter' was trimming ewes on a table in a long sheep shed; behind him two of the regular men were brushing up his next sheep, and two more were paring feet in the pens. There were some very nice ewes in the sale—it looked as if the best were going, but they were of course in better order than the sheep we saw outside.

It was noon when we rejoined Miss Carter—she was going to drive us back to Staunton, but we asked to be dropped somewhere for a walk, saying that we would get ourselves home in the evening. Miss Carter protested that we could not possibly walk—she would drive us up on to the Blue Ridge Mountains for a look round, but unfortunately she had work to do in the afternoon, or nothing would have pleased her better than to drive us all day. By the time we had bounced along the by-road to the Mountain in a tightly closed car, the point at issue was settled by my inside, and I was deposited green on to the roadside while Mary tried to convince Miss Carter that we would really enjoy a good long walk in that beautiful country. We were now at the bottom of Blue Ridge and a compromise was reached—we were driven slowly to the top with the car window open, and left by a rather anxious Miss Carter to walk along the Ridge and meet her at the end of it in the evening. Her insistence on driving out of town again to collect such an odd couple of strangers was typical of the warm kindliness we met everywhere in the States.

That walk was unforgettable. The wind was like a knife—we were over a thousand feet up, on top of the Blue Ridge Mountains. Below us to the west lay the Shenandoah Valley, with the distant Alleghenny Mountains beyond; to the east another blue plain and far mountains, whose names we could not find on our map. On either side of the ridge the ground dropped sheer away in tree-clad hillsides—we kept peering down for bears, but wild turkeys—a gobbler and four hens—were the only game we saw. Here and there observation posts were cut in the woods, giving an even better view of the stretching country below—there were some maps in wooden holders, and lists of animals which might be seen, and a brief history of the settling of these parts; but we did not feel like trippers in this most beautiful National Park, which at this time of the year was almost deserted—only two cars passed us.

Next morning, a very cold one, we got into the front seats of the bus for our drive up the Shenandoah Valley—the first time we had achieved this vantage point which gives an uninterrupted forward view, and in this case the incessant conversation of the driver who had memories of war-time Piccadilly! However, we gleaned also some information about the route, which ran through a ribbon of uninteresting villages joined together by endless odd shacks and small farm houses. The road crossed and re-crossed the 'rolling river', which was smaller than one had imagined from the song, and quieter—in places a rather sluggish stream. The famous valley was disappointing, giving no hint of the magnificent panorama to be seen from the Blue Ridge above. The run was pleasant, however, and smooth—fast, but quite unhurried, for he was a first class driver; and there were few enough passengers for general country greetings and chat as people got on and off to go shopping or visit their neighbours up and down the road. After three hours we ourselves dismounted at The Plains, a very small wayside village; we felt abandoned in the wilds as the friendly bus drove on for Washington. However, very soon a girl in slacks crossed the road—it was Mrs. Eldredge, and our most delightful visit had begun.

We were driven about 4 miles in a big Buick station wagon through country lanes to a house where we felt instantly at home. It was not beautiful outside, but stone built and solid, with a paved terrace and some steps up to the front door. Inside it was gracious, with good furniture and wide windows and no blinds to hide the pleasant view beyond. Hunting prints hung in the hall and up the shallow stairway—hunting in Virginia means fox-hunting as we know it—hounds meet four days a week and Mrs. Eldredge had two horses. A couple of beautiful Irish setters rose from their rug in the lounge to greet us—the dog Peter grinned a welcome like dog Flax, but they were afraid to come on to the polished wood floor of the hall. Mr. Eldredge gave us the first good sherry we had tasted in America and we went in to lunch. An old coloured butler served a delicious meal on a beautiful polished table; but for him and our glasses of cold milk we might have been in an English country house.

We had first heard of Mr. Eldredge from Marian. She bought from him the good Montadale ram lamb that has left such a mark on her cross-bred flock—he was then farming in Connecticut, and we did not know that before he moved to Virginia the whole of his Montadale flock was slaughtered by government order because he had a case of scrapie. The Montadale was a comparatively new breed, evolved by putting a Cheviot ram on Columbia ewes—the Columbia is related to the Merino. The result is a very nice sheep: white faced, sharp and upstanding, with strong clean legs and a good coat. The type seems fixed, but there were not many flocks and the loss of one of the best was a sore blow. Replacement was difficult, and Mr. Eldredge was very particular. He had only about half a dozen pure bred Montadale ewes, but they were most beautiful sheep: one year-ling ewe was especially outstanding. They were running with a few pedigree Suffolk ewes—the original Suffolk flock was also lost—but here replacement was easier, though it would not be quick, for only the best would do.

We drove round the farm in a jeep, up and down some mighty banks and beside fine woods through which the cattle go down to the brook to drink. The land was ideal for sheep, and very much in leys. The greatest attention was paid to change for the sheep, and in time, of course, the commercial flock would give way to the pedigrees.

When the homestead buildings were finished there was to be a milking unit, an implement shed, and open-fronted lambing pens, with easy access to the meadows adjoining. Only the implement shed was ready and this was filled with deep litter poultry to earn dividends until the rest was finished.

Tea was a most homely meal round a wood fire, with delicious tea from a pot (no bags!) and talk of sheep and cattle, dogs and horses, breeding and feeding, until it was time for our bus. When we reached the village we sat in the car for nearly an hour, still talking, until suddenly the bus loomed up in the darkness and we were whisked away to Washington with the talk unfinished but the American trip complete. There could not have been a happier ending.

We travelled back to New York next morning, found an hotel near the docks, and then walked to Lexington Avenue to collect sailing permits from the Income Tax people—as we had earned no dollars there was no difficulty here. We then walked Fifth Avenue in a hunt for wild rice and presents for everyone. We at last tracked down the wild rice in Macey's, which is not on Fifth Avenue at all, but on Fourth, we think. It was a vast and noisy department store, with a weird bell constantly clanging and Father Christmas everywhere. The heat in the stores was terrific, and we were thankful to return to the hotel (still walking) just in time to meet Marian and Bill for dinner. Marian was triumphant with her successful luggage delivery at the docks, and full of news and mail for us—it was lovely to see them again. We took them afterwards to 'Joyce Grenfell requests the pleasure...' and enjoyed ourselves immensely, though still regretting the full house of 'Cat on a Hot Tin Roof'. Afterwards we walked up Broadway, looking at the lights and pictures of other shows until it was time to cross for our hotel. We arranged to meet again on the docks next morning.

We were up early after a good night. It seemed odd to start such a long journey by walking—we had breakfast in a drug store on the way, reached the docks about 9 o'clock, and went straight aboard with no formalities, to find our luggage waiting for us in an even

Farewell to Marian and Bill on board Britannic

better cabin than we had before. Marian and Bill arrived at last—we were a bit anxious that they would not have much time with us, but visitors were allowed to stay almost till we sailed, and it is surprising that some did not get left, for there were no warning bells. We explored the ship together, took some photographs and watched the towering Queen Mary, again tied alongside Britannic as we had seen her from the Empire State Building a month before. Marian and Bill wisely left the docks when they went ashore—we wondered when we should see them again.

At 11 a.m. one tug nosed under the Queen Mary's bows and pushed her stern first into the river; she swung downstream at right angles and was away—like a taxi turning in the street. Quarter of an hour later we followed her, with as little fuss; but she was soon out of sight, due home in five days to our eight—I was sad we had not sailed in her.

We slid quietly down the river; we watched Wall Street dropping astern but missed the Statue of Liberty for a most desultory boat drill on the port side of the prom. deck. This was the last effort we had to make for over a week, and we settled down to a most enjoyable routine. The sea was dead calm over the week-end and though the swell on Monday disturbed me somewhat we never missed sitting on our deck chairs in the open. Towards the end of the voyage progress seemed slow—Britannic was due for a refit, and we lost time. We made Cobh at night instead of noon as expected, so failed to see that fine harbour; but it was fun to watch the pilot come aboard in the dark, especially when a flood light fell into the sea when the poor man was in mid-ladder! Our amusement indicates the monotony of even the best Atlantic crossing. We sailed quietly on into the harbour with the lights of houses on either side, and met the Cobh tender about 10 p.m. Passengers were exchanged—we were sorry for ours, set down in a strange town in the small hours—and a car and heaps of luggage unloaded. We watched for a long time, but were in bed before we again got under way—one more night, and then home!

Drizzle and a grey sky next morning, and we felt very close—then the cliffs and fields of Anglesey on the starboard bow, and we were peering for sheep and thinking of Armscote Marquis up there, and all the Wiltshire Horn flocks we knew. At midday we picked up the senior Liverpool pilot from a small boat in choppy water—the Britannic was the largest ship to berth at Liverpool, and the senior pilot always took her in. We sailed up the line of buoys, past the anchored oil tankers waiting to go in, crossed the Bar before we had expected, and there at last was Liverpool. We landed in darkness and steady rain, but nothing dampened our joy. The train looked like a toy after the massive American rolling stock, but we thought proudly that here was a British express that would arrive on time—it went straight through to Hereford, and was over forty minutes late! Nothing mattered—we were home—comparisons are odious, but we realised more and more as the days went by what a fine people we had been privileged to visit, what fun it all was, and what a great country we have seen.

IX
Smallholders

We walked into the Brook Farm house at midnight on Friday December 9th, 1955 and inside the door to welcome us was a joyous dog Flax. It was a supreme moment: Pamela and Raymond had brought him on the bus from Presteigne instead of coming to work on the motorbike as usual; a kind thought which made all the difference to our homecoming. We were surprised to find the house so small—not that Craholla was large, but Brook Farm was tiny. The empty buildings seemed strange and to have no cow to milk was a great miss. We collected the bitches and the two lots of sheep as soon as possible and set about stocking up: four little pigs from Ledicot, two to sell when reared, two to keep as sows; a house cow and her calf from Hereford market, soon to be joined by two more for calf suckling; and three little store cattle, also from Hereford, to run in the covered yard until we were able to fill this with calves of our own rearing. Each cow reared five calves a lactation, two, two, and one, while the rich stripping milk was set in flat pans on the larder slab, skimmed daily, and the cream made into butter by Pamela, using a glass jar churn with paddles. The pigs drank the skim, mixed with a little meal, household scraps and small potatoes cooked overnight in the Aga oven and mashed in the buckets so that the whole feed was warm—a lot of work but nothing wasted.

Helen had looked after things well in our absence, but was troubled by the small boy, who blotted his copy book good and proper; we sent him off with two weeks wages. Helen stayed on a while part

Mary, Flirt and show ewes in the yard at Brook Farm, 1956

time, but was soon to be married, and we were concerned to find someone responsible who would do our work when we were away showing. The problem was solved when the house next door fell vacant, we were able to buy it, and in April '56 Raymond and Pamela moved into The Pentre.

This amazing stroke of luck set our labour right for a while: Pamela was our cook-housekeeper as of old; when we were away Raymond milked and saw to all the stock before and after his saw mills work; and Arthur came down from Lucton with his little tractor and trailer as required. The hedges were hand trimmed by Mr. Donnelly, who biked from Kingsland of an evening; (this work lasted from June till September and was bad for late-nesting birds—we don't start now with the machine until late August and it takes one day!) Then there were the 'Saturday morning boys', a gang of three which lasted for years, changing personnel as the elder got bored or left school, when the younger would co-opt a mate ('Young Billy Barnes would do, Miss'—'Bring him along and we'll see.') We got through an immense amount of work with them, chiefly mucking out the cattle pens with fork and wheelbarrow. Mary taught them how to build a tidy mixon: the top straw in a pen is pulled back and the well-soaked strong-smelling bottom straw removed and built into a straight sided well trodden muck heap, which rises like a hay rick, the middle slightly higher than the sides, to run off rain. The whole is compressed by treading to exclude air and hasten rotting. In the pen the top straw is replaced to the bottom and a generous layer of new straw added and replenished as necessary: the state of the litter and the time and labour available determine how often the pens are mucked out. 'Deep Litter' is no new method of stock keeping.

The boys each had a pay packet dating from the week before and were punctual and cheerful (or else!) and we collected a lot of football news; but it was a most exhausting exercise for us.

We needed to reduce the heavy work with the fold units, to increase egg production, and to make use of the funny little Dutch barn at The Pentre, which backed on to our buildings and orchard. We planned a deep litter laying house of original design which Norman Shock, a Kingsland freelance handyman, followed beautifully: a long lean-to on the side of our lorry shed ran through the over large Pentre garden and opened into the barn, making a sizeable L-shaped building which in turn opened into a large outside run in the orchard. The lean-to was built with pleasant old red bricks, cheaper then than now, and roofed with asbestos sheets, lined inside with fibreglass. There was a generous number of hopper windows, removed from the Brook Farm house and stored carefully, with glass intact. The floor of the lean-to was left as beaten earth, in theory better for litter working than the concrete of the barn, but in practice more difficult to muck out. The litter was sawdust, about a foot deep, easily obtained (but heavy to haul) from Kingsland saw mills. Electricity and water were handy from either dwelling house, a long range of nest boxes was built in, and we reckoned that 'Deep Litter Bottom' would carry 200 hens, with another 50 in 'Deep Litter Top'. This was the upper storey of the little barn, with a wooden floor and huge windows, up to which we climbed on a ladder three times daily, carrying a grain bucket and an egg container and pushing open an overhead hatch as we went. It sounds crazy, but the whole set-up worked, the hens laid well and were happy and in all the years we kept free of epidemic disease.

Our building experience was much helped by Frank Roberts' work on the milking parlour and yards at Brook Bridge: he conferred constantly with us, as landlords, and we learned a lot. His help transformed our haymaking and the little farm swung along, all in grass, fully stocked, and above all carrying a successful flock of

Sheila, Verney Pugh, Mary and Wendy at the North Brecon Show, Builth, 1957

pedigree sheep. In 1957 we won the Leominster agricultural society's Milton Cup for the best managed farm of under 100 acres.

Then came a great blow: Raymond and Pamela announced that they would be leaving us in a week's time for a rented cottage in Kingsland. We heard a rumour the day before they told us and couldn't believe it, but it was true and they went. With hindsight we realise that they were afraid that Pamela, with babies coming, would be unable to continue working for us and that we would want the house for someone else—the lurking bogey of the tied cottage; but we would never have turned them out. We lost touch with them for a while, but are thankful to have had them with us now for the last nineteen years.

Pamela came back to us each day while we had no help in the house, but this was only just over a week: with incredible good fortune for us Idwell and Frances were on the move. Recommended strongly by friends of ours for whom Frances had worked for many years, they needed now a home of their own. Their furniture was out of store and into The Pentre in no time and we had responsible neighbours again. Idwell worked in a Leominster garage but helped us with odd handyman jobs about the house and was always ready to drive us in case of emergency—they had a good old bull-nosed Morris of which they were very proud. Frances, for all her frailty, was our most excellent cook-housekeeper for ten years and then stayed on in the Pentre after Idwell's sudden death and our move up to Lucton, until she went to live near her daughter's family in Cambridge. She died some years later.

There remained still the problem of finding someone to help us outside and to take charge of the stock in our absence. We advertised for a more mature and educated girl and Pauline (not her real name) came up from the South. An attractive, red-haired girl, she had been a secretary but longed for a country life and work with animals. We liked her, there was all winter to train her with the stock, her secretarial skill might be useful and she was keen for the job. We took her on, found her lodgings with friends near-by, and

With yearling ewes at Knighton Show, 1958

within a week she could milk and was happy with the cows, as we were with her.

Unfortunately the Beehive was not quite finished when Pauline came. This was our second deep litter house, designed to take another 250 hens, bringing our flock up to 500, with each house emptied, cleaned and re-stocked in alternate years. We built it with 'Woodcemair' panels—light slabs of wood shavings mixed with cement and air, set between oak posts, with large high windows down both sides, two sets of double doors and an insulated asbestos roof. A central ventilator looking like a beehive was set on the roof top. The walls were plastered inside and out, and painted white, with dark green doors—it was a pleasant building which made a splendid sheep shed in later years.

The gipsy-handsome Gerald was completing last minute jobs in the Beehive during Pauline's first days with us. He was a skilled free-lance craftsman who lived in Leominster with wife and family and roamed round the country doing odd jobs which took his fancy. He finished off the Beehive beautifully, departed, and we thought no more of him until four weeks later, after Pauline's first long weekend off. Her landlady, who, to her shame, had read a private letter, reported a raging affair between Pauline and Gerald.

We felt responsible for Pauline: perhaps in these days one wouldn't, but we are glad that we did. We talked to her and asked her plans—she was frank, tearful and totally unrealistic: she and Gerald would go away together and when his divorce came through they would marry. With her permission we telephoned her mother, and then arranged a Sunday evening meeting for Gerald and Pauline in our house. We started with Mary in the kitchen, comforting a distraught Pauline, and me in the dining room, talking to a gentle, dignified Gerald. Then we sent Pauline in to him and made ourselves scarce: they left together a while later.

On the Monday morning Pauline's mother travelled up from the South and in the afternoon they returned home together: Pauline had been with us just over six weeks. She wrote to us later that she was working happily for a country bookseller who took a caravan round the shows.

Our good fortune held: four days later Enid Postans came to see about our job. Mary was in bed after a hospital tooth extraction, two of our three cows calved that day and I was overwhelmed with worry, work and weariness. Enid came as a god-send. She was a capable country girl, a smallholder's daughter who could milk, and I knew she was right for us. She started work a week later and was with us for nearly six years, during which came our greatest show successes with the sheep.

We needed another small enterprise to help pay wages and achieved one almost by chance: one of our small land purchases, an acre of cider orchard opposite the Hopyard meadow, had been owned by a Hereford fruit merchant who underplanted it with thousands of daffodil and narcissus bulbs. We had to find a market for the flowers and were delighted when the manager of a large retail store in Hereford offered us a shilling a bunch 'for as many as you like', to be delivered early on market day morning. The day before we picked and picked, in warm sunshine, with the bees working and the sweet narcissus scent heavy in the air. Enid was a good quick picker—so was Mary and they enjoyed it together. There were so many flowers that first day that we called in some casual workers by the hour. Each bunch was of twelve blooms, secured in two places with tiny rubber bands carried by the pickers, either on the fingers (Mary) or in a box in the pocket. The bunches were laid in the rows, to be collected in armfulls, mostly by me, carried to the van, driven up the road and plunged in water in the cool dark garage—innumerable jars, buckets and baths were rustled up for the purpose, and still the bunches kept coming—over a thousand of them. Towards evening we rang the store to check that they really would take all we brought—the answer was yes, so we carried on.

Next morning, very early, Mary and I counted the bunches into soft fruit trays (we had bought a large number of these for damsons when a wholesaler gave up), stacked them high in the van and I drove off to Hereford. At the store I reported arrival and asked for unloading help: the man in charge (not he who had done the deal) gave me a flat refusal. I begged 'Can't you take some of them?' 'None' he replied, 'couldn't sell them'. He was adamant—I think he didn't want the work. I felt desperate, but set off round every flower or fruit shop that I could find. Some were helpful, some were not—none would buy a bunch. At last I was directed to try the Butter Market, in the centre of the city: in a daze I walked through the huge hall among stalls of all kinds, already crowded with buyers, until I came on a large central one with a high gold notice: V. BROUGHTON above it and a kind-looking woman underneath. She was busy selling beautiful flowers but had time to pause to hear my tale of woe. She glanced at my tray of narcissus and said 'Bring them in, love. Shan't be able to sell them all but we'll try—only sixpence a bunch to you, I'm afraid...' I could have kissed her for twopence! She sent a girl to help me unload —together we carried the many trays through the busy hall, transferred the bunches into buckets of water ranged in a cool dark cellar beneath the stall, and carried the empties back to the van. When we had finished Mrs. Broughton accepted my count and paid me what seemed a great deal of money in £1 notes. 'Give me a ring when you have some more' she said, 'but be sure to bring them the day before market.' That was the beginning of our long and valued trading with Mrs. Vera Broughton and her daughter Pauline. I drove home in triumph to Mary and a very late breakfast.

Now that we had an assured market we could plan the flower growing with more intelligence. We dug and worked the third pig paddock and tried various annuals, such as cornflowers (tedious to bunch); dahlias (a pleasure and profitable but not good travellers); everlasting flowers (shy croppers), larkspurs and anemones. Tulip bulbs did well the first year but failed to persist. In the end we found that by far the best bet was Dutch Iris: Wedgewood, the pale blue early one, and Imperator, dark purple and later. They were up in the rows and could be hoed in November, needed only to be kept clean, and were easy to pick and bunch. The first year we made the mistake of letting the flowers open before picking: a disastrous thunder storm ruined most of them, while the rest suffered damage in transit. Mrs. Broughton taught us to pick them as soon as the buds showed a streak of blue, when they would store for days in water in a dark cool building and market to perfection as the flowers opened. We picked daily and took a load of buds each week from mid-May to early June. On Mrs. B's advice we gave up the annuals and invested in a large number of Dutch Iris which paid us well for many years and multiplied, so that when we moved to Lucton we brought with us bags full of bulbs to replant in the large garden at Hill Croft.

With increased work and income we thought that the place would carry another girl, to help with hoeing and mucking out and to relieve our routine when Enid was off. Our show success brought us many sheep customers and we were increasingly busy throughout the year. We advertised, and Celia came with her mother to see if she would do. We thought so and took her on, without realising fully the extent of our new responsibility. Celia was with us on and off for several years and wore down on one side many brooms with her vigorous yard sweeping. (We have still a lop-sided one whose name is Celia.) We considered seriously providing her with a chalet when we moved to Lucton, but she had other plans and finally left us for good.

For some years our various enterprises kept us in credit, but in 1962-63 our farm account showed a loss. This must be checked immediately—we considered carefully what to do. Egg prices were falling but we had no room nor wish to increase the hens; rams were becoming more difficult to sell as fashion began to swing away from the Kerry Hill; wages were rising but we would need more, not less, help as time went on. Worst of all, our hay-making was going wrong. Frank Roberts had reduced his work force and two of his sons had begun to take over. They were not party to our gentleman's agreement with Frank, and naturally tended towards their own work, leaving ours behind. Frank himself may have been starting to feel the onset of the Parkinson's Disease which he and his Mary fought together so long and with such courage.

We talked through our own retirement: definitely we were not ready for it, and anyway what would we do with ourselves? We were sure that we must expand again, with an experienced man and an enterprise that would bring a better and steadier income: at that time a dairy herd was the money maker for the small farmer, and we had almost a ready made set-up at Brook Bridge.

Very tentatively we approached Frank Roberts: he was understanding as always and to our surprise was quite ready to hand back Brook Bridge—his boys were not interested in stock and they were expanding the arable at Ledicot. It was arranged in the autumn of 1963 that we should take over at Lady Day (March 25th) 1964.

We met Veronica one day in Hereford Market (scene of several confidences between us, including her engagement to Tony Sanger) and told her our news. She looked at us aghast and said 'You must be crazy'. In a way I suppose she was right: it was the biggest and most frightening experience of our life together, but we agree that we would not have missed it.

X
The Dairy Herd

Through the winter of 1963-64 we laid our plans. We asked and received from the bank a substantial loan—we lived successfully on an overdraft for the next four years. With the help of Messrs. F. Dale of Leominster we planned an extension to the three-bay Dutch barn at Brook Bridge—the long north side would be thrown out into half the barren kitchen garden below, with a lean-to roof, breeze-block walls and a wide feeding and driving passage with doors at either end, giving ample winter lying room for the forty cow herd to be. The plans were finalised in winter, Dales started work on May 25th and finished on June 17th, just in time for bale hauling into the barn under cover: we were all very proud of that building.

We ordered new hay making machinery—a Massey-Ferguson tractor (£635), mowing machine, side-rake, tedder and a New Holland baler (£520) all with handsome discounts for early delivery.

Then came the most important thing of all: on Boxing Day we composed our advertisement for a 'First-class young man to help build and take charge of a new small commercial dairy herd'. We had so many replies that we sent a questionnaire to some of the more promising (one of the questions was 'do you smoke?', which brought a furious letter from a chap who challenged our right to ask such a thing.) We interviewed several—(one in Buckinghamshire, where I went to see a customer's flock and she was kind enough to offer that hospitality.) Then Frank Haynes brought his wife and two small children to see us: he was very experienced, we liked him a lot and they seemed to like us. We offered him the job, he accepted, and we felt immensely relieved to have cleared that important hurdle. A few days later he rang and cried off and we were much depressed—the momentum of the advertisement was lost, we were tired of interviewing, and that fierce winter had begun to bite, with snow and 18 degrees of frost on January 14th. But on the 22nd there was a thaw, Eric Stradling rang from Somerset and after a merry conversation we decided that we must see him.

Owing to the weather Mary had just cancelled an expedition to Ilfracombe with her young nephew Graham Beach for company, to recover an unpaid-for ram lamb. Graham had returned to Bootham School but sister Ruth would come (Mary and I could not get away together at that time of year) and the Stradlings could be visited on the way down—Eric was managing his mother's herd near Frome.

All plans went well: the ram was picked up without a fuss and Mary returned full of enthusiasm for Eric, a fair, curly-headed young man with a tremendously hearty laugh. He had been on his parents' farm since leaving school and had taken charge of the herd since his father's death. Now married, with a small daughter, he wanted a better house, more money and he saw our job for the challenge that it was. We arranged that he and his family should come to see us in Kingsland as soon as possible, and on February 1st 1964 he brought Ann and Nicola, then aged two, to lunch with us at Brook Farm. Afterwards we walked the farms, looked carefully at the Brook Bridge house, where we planned some improvements, and then at the buildings. In the milking parlour our new Alfa-Laval milking machine was being fitted by kind Mr. Coyne, of Dairy Supplies Hereford. Here we had everything to learn and Eric was able to help us with suggestions, though we did not succumb to his pressure to fit a unit for all six stalls: we knew that four cows to milk at once was enough for us to learn the job—the other two units came later.

We returned to tea at Brook Farm, talked over and fixed a starting salary acceptable to all and offered Eric the job. He agreeed readily and they left us at 6 p.m. to drive back to Frome, while we went about our stock work, tired but happy, confident that we had found the right man at last.

Eric and his family moved into Brook Bridge in April; on May 8th we bought our first three heifers and on the 9th we sold our first milk—9 gallons in one churn—we were thrilled to bits! We decided to go steady with spring calvers and build up to forty in the autumn, when the milk price was rising. Each Friday we went to Hereford, the three of us in the lorry, our cheerful talk punctuated by Eric's hearty laugh. Arrived in market we would separate, going up and down the long line of cows and heifers tied in the lairage, looking first at udders, then at eyes and aspect, before moving in to try the teats, with often a passing word to each other ('Try No. 38—but watch your knees—she nearly had me'). Then we would compare notes, decide on four or five that would do, and find ourselves a good place in the sale ring, half way up the tiers in front of the auctioneer. We went for the best Friesian heifers we could find—at that time there were some beauties coming in, brought by men who made a business of calving them down to a Hereford bull and keeping the calves to raise as stores. We bid openly, often topped the trade and of course were run up by the owners; but we made a point of stopping suddenly every now and then, so they got used to us and I think we achieved a fair average at about £120 apiece throughout, (though once a farmer in hospital received the news that Wenham and Elliott paid £150 for a heifer!) It was all great fun and the auctioneers liked us and went out of their way to help. Once, when we followed out a recent purchase to ease her milk, she had disappeared: Messrs. Russell, Baldwin and Bright scoured the market, traced her to Abergavenny, and sent to fetch her back for us, with Terry Court and Julian Gallimore themselves travelling in the lorry to make sure all was well. The heifer Chestnut was returned next day none the worse, and we were much relieved: many of these heifers had never seen a milking machine and Eric's initial breaking-in was all important— he was very good at it. Despite her trip Chestnut soon settled down, helped by the quiet temperament we looked for—we did not make many mistakes, though Violet had to wear a kicking strap, fastened firmly round her middle in front of the udder, so that the act of kicking was painful (a cow always kicks forwards or sideways, never back) and she learned to stand still.

For a month after we began Eric never missed a milking while he taught Mary to use the machine: then she and I milked together when we relieved him and Mary taught me; but I never really got used to it. I found the intense concentration against the inexorable pulsing of the machine desperately tiring, with the anxiety that the teat cups would be left on too long, thereby inducing mastitis, or not long enough, so that the yield would be reduced. Each cow, as she enters her stall, must have her correct feed ration, checked by a quick glance at the written table above the standings. The feed was scooped from hopper to manger with a long handled shovel and the holding chain linked behind her, the udder then wiped with a tepid sterile cloth, a few squirts of milk taken from each teat into a strip cup and inspected, and the four teat cups fitted. As she finished milking the teat cups were removed, the cluster hung up, her yield recorded, and each teat was dipped in an oily disinfectant as a further safeguard against the dreaded mastitis. Then the release lever was pulled, she went out at the front, the rear chain was dropped and the next cow eagerly took her place. I often wonder at the chatty gossip in which the Archers indulge during milking.

Meanwhile the relentless machine went on and on—except when it didn't! Ours was new and good and we had little trouble: once we had to fetch Eric from the field when we were milking for him during hay hauling; but it was something we had done wrong and he soon righted that. Freezing up on bitter winter mornings was a nightmare; but an electricity cut was worst of all. On a winter night the parlour was suddenly plunged in darkness: there was a moment's deathly silence, then all six clusters plopped one by one to the floor: another silence, then six more plops as each cow lifted her tail and mucked on to the floor all over the fallen clusters. Then one of us hastened to telephone the Electricity Board while the other cleared

Eric strip cupping

up as best she could by torchlight. After that there was nothing to do but wait. We were lucky that our longest cut was only about two hours—I shudder to think how we would have managed in the interminable cuts after the '87 hurricane. We talked often of getting a generator to run off the tractor but never got around to it: we had more than our share of lucky escapes.

We milked at 6 morning and evening: at 7.30 a.m., after feeding the pigs (we reared porkers now, to make use of the daily strippings and the occasional mastitis milk) I biked up to Brook Bridge to meet Eric as he finished milking. He reported any troubles, what cows were bulling, and the amount of milk to go that day: we discussed rations, prices, which field to graze and his work for the day—too much talk when he was tired and longing for his breakfast, but I had my own work to get through and there was no other time. Then he went in to Ann; Celia or Enid came up to sweep the yards, and I drove the cows out to graze. When they went to Brook Farm fields Mary met us on the bridge and we took them down the road together, fetching them back in the evening when the girls had gone and Eric was having his tea. This was a slow and tranquil progress which we enjoyed—the cows were never hurried, no dog came near them and we could admire their wealthy bags and shining coats as they wandered along the road.

Another magic time for us was 'supping up' at 10 on a winter's night when Eric was off: one of us would walk quietly up and down the wide feeding passage between barn and cows, pikling back into the manger the hay which they had spilled and watching contented creatures as they lay in deep straw chewing their cud, or strolled up to the barrier to see what was coming in. We could believe then that the animals knelt to pay tribute on Christmas Eve.

Before the cows came in for their first winter we gave a house warming party in the new building, inviting several of our younger farming neighbours to meet Eric and Ann: at least one lasting friendship followed and we were glad, for it was lonely for Ann at Brook Bridge while Eric was at work. We were all overjoyed when John William Stradling was born on January 2nd 1965. We milked for Eric that day.

Eric announced on his first day with us: 'I'm no union man', and indeed his work hours were awful—6 in the morning till 8 at night, with three hours off for meals (but often he didn't take so long) and in winter an extra excursion at 10 p.m. to 'sup up'. Calves came at all times and he was always on the ball, though we tried to ease him here when he was busy with silage or hay. He had one day off a week, after morning milking, and a long weekend a month, adjusted to the season and our showing. His holiday was also adjustable and a hard job for us to manage—we were thankful to welcome him back.

Silage making was new to us: at first we tried gathering the wilted grass with a buck rake behind the tractor and clamping it near the gate of the chosen field. The clamp was made with portable wooden walls, supported by stout iron stays bolted on—Arthur helped Eric set it up and shift it. In winter the day's ration of silage was cut out with a hay knife and hauled to the feeding passage in the tractor's link box; but the ground at the clamp became so cut up that after two years struggle we built a silage barn alongside the cows' building and hauled the ration round on the concrete on a four wheel hand trolley; but it still had to be cut out, a job we never attempted: two days supply was cut before Sundays and free days, and at Eric's long weekends Arthur came down to do it. We progressed also to a cutter blower and tipping trailer instead of mowing machine and buck rake, which eased the harvesting and meant that we could cut for silage right round the farms.

Another job where we could have saved labour but didn't was the home mixing of the cows' parlour ration. This was a coarse mix, based on rolled oats, flaked maize and bran, with concentrated dairy nuts added sparingly, according to price, season and milk yield—the ration varied from field to field as we changed the grazing. The cows milked wonderfully well and we did not want to press them with overmuch expensive cake.

Thanks to Frank Roberts, the lay-out of the parlour building was ideal. He had made use of the rising ground to form a concrete apron in front of the dairy and meal house, set above the existing farmyard at lorry bed level: bags of corn and cake were unloaded easily and wheeled in, while churns were rolled out and on to a purpose built trolley of the right height; the trolley was pulled by hand down the yard and the churns were rolled off on to a same level sleeper platform built on the roadside. This was a precarious operation, especially with six or eight full churns: it always took two of us, but Eric managed on his own. Once—but only once—a churn tipped off—we've forgotten who was wheeling. The delivered empty churns were trolleyed back before evening milking—a lot of work, but at that time Cadburys would collect only from the roadside, a problem for isolated farms and in hot weather: the advent of bulk tanks was a tremendous change for the better.

Cash flowed faster as milk sales grew and we began to sell calves. We used A.I. through the Milk Marketing Board, who stood several first rate Hereford bulls. Their calves out of Friesian cows are black, with white faces and stout bodies, and were very fashionable at the time as future store cattle. Our calves ran with their mothers for about ten days—we never sold a calf under a week old. Each Wednesday in the season one of us drove those who were ready to Hereford in the van and stood over them in the crowded calf pens until they went singly through the auction ring. This way customers got to know us and the type of calf we brought, and our trade was good—we often topped £30 for strong bull calves, a great price in those days.

As our sales grew so did Eric's wages; but his requests for more money nearly always preceded our carefully budgetted rises, and we felt pressured and dug in our toes. He and Ann could not make ends meet and their local debts worried us greatly. More worrying still was Eric's growing tiredness: he stayed out longer than ever in the evenings attending to calvers, scrubbing down the immaculate dairy, and completing endless small jobs which would have gone better in the morning. When he got in he was almost too tired to eat and fell asleep before he finished: 'I want my husband' Ann said to me once. We realised that this could not go on.

It is a paradox that while 'single handed' milking is about the only way a young couple can make a start in farming, yet it is a potential destroyer of family life. The endless grind of seven hundred and thirty milkings a year gets everyone down in the end.

Eric was not quite single handed and the ultimate responsibility was not his; but we ourselves could not give him enough relief. We had hoped that Enid would take to machine milking—and how good she would have been—but she would have none of it, and after another year or so she left. Celia kept on sweeping up and littering down, but could progress no further. We offered Eric a boy to train, but no—he would prefer the money himself. It seemed the end of the road.

We talked it through and through and round and round. Among the cows one day Eric said: 'What would happen to all this if I go?' I replied 'We should sell up.' He looked sad and said 'A pity...' I think we had not quite faced it before, but we knew that we were nearly at the end of our own tether, though we had to choose our time. I had another long talk with Eric when he was rolling the Monument ground on the far side of Brook Farm: I stopped him and stood leaning against the tractor in warm spring sunshine while we ranged through the fields of our philosophies. I think he would have stayed with us had we pressed him, and if we had known what lay next ahead we would not have had the courage to let him go.

We advertised again for a herdsman but had very few replies: the only one possible seemed to be from Ron, (not his real name) a suave plausible fellow with limited experience but willing to learn, he said. We had no choice—time was running out and we knew that we could not manage for long on our own. The first pointer to our mistake was the amazed relief of his wife when we offered him the job. With their two small boys they moved into Brook Bridge the day after Eric left.

Mary milked with Ron for some time before she felt she could leave him on his own, and Frances was taken to hospital the day after he arrived, so that the strain on us was very great. We soon found that he would not bother with calvings out of hours, so we had to take that on ourselves.

We arranged with him before he came that we would have a bull, as he did not want the responsibility of calling for A.I. at the right time, nor would we have trusted him to do so. We were able to buy for £150 a nice young Hereford bull, Marlow Oliver, from Sidney Owens' son John. Oliver got all our cows in calf so that they were just right for our dispersal sale: he was lovely to handle and so quiet that he never had a ring in his nose.

We had entered sheep as usual for the summer shows of '66 and held to our schedule, though with growing anxiety. Silage and hay making were difficult, though Arthur helped us a lot: we were none

149

Marlow Oliver resting from the dairy herd

of us used to the new silage machinery and Ron was not clever with
it. One day, as I biked from the field where Arthur was cutting to see
how Ron was doing in the new silage barn, I heard mad screeching
and found two tiny boys and their shrieking mother clambering up
and down on the lumpy mound of silage, with Ron on the lurching
tractor towering above them as he rolled down the unstable mass of
grass. I felt in a nightmare world and my vehemence as I ordered
them off did not improve relations.

Ron became more and more rude and careless: in the autumn we
lost a calf in day time because he failed to wait and get it to suck.
Arthur's unspoken sympathy and support helped greatly, but we all
knew that we could not go on like this. In time we realised that Ron
was a beastly man and we were anxious for the cows. We laid our
plans, but hesitated to give him the sack before Christmas, partly for

lack of a proven reason, partly because of the difficulty of getting a supply milker over the holidays. To our immense relief the matter was resolved when Ron gave us notice on Boxing Day because he had to milk over Christmas. We had given him the choice of which day to have off, and he chose Boxing Day so that he could get his shooting. He left without saying goodbye, and we felt sane again; but the affair had taken its toll: I have not yet got rid of the rising panic which hits me sometimes and which Mary helps me so wonderfully to control.

We had decided to sell the herd in the following autumn, when the cows should be at their peak: meanwhile we would manage with a succession of relief milkers, who were supplied by an agency and supposed to change every month. As soon as the Christmas holiday was over we contacted Mayday Milking Services in Surrey, and on January 26th 1967 Henry Lock arrived.

Henry was a big quiet man in his early thirties: he liked our cows and was gentle with them and in accord with us—an immense relief after the unhappiness with Ron, which far outweighed the practical problems of our new arrangements. We were responsible for Henry's board and lodging: there were two available houses but no cook. Recently our tenant Mrs. Woodhouse had moved from the cottage next door to Frances and we had furnished it very simply as a guest house for our friends. We put Henry there for a few nights until we could move a little of this furniture into the empty Brook Bridge house, right on the job. We could not ask Frances for anything extra—she was just managing heroically, between her bouts of illness, to cook a mid-day meal for us; so Mary cooked Henry's breakfast and Ethel at The Willows took on his dinner, which we fetched each day at quarter to one, putting the covered dishes into his Rayburn oven to keep warm till he came. We stocked Henry's larder, he got his own supper and was wonderfully good in washing up and keeping tidy: Mary made his bed at breakfast time and one of us swept through the house during the day. Meanwhile our shepherding and other work continued as well, though of course we abandoned showing for that year. The milk yield rose again, the cows were fine and we had little relief milking, as Henry declared that while he was here he would do it.

When he had been with us nearly a month we asked him whether he would stay on and take us up to our October sale, despite the Mayday rules. He agreed and we were thankful. We arranged to hire another relief milker so that he could have a fortnight's holiday in July, after haymaking, and we were able to give him a long weekend in May. Through the summer his girlfriend and his parents came severally to stay at the Woodhouse as our guests. Henry drove them out for days off but was always back for milking; and the herd prospered.

During that spring we had another heavy blow: Frances was taken to hospital and never worked for us again, though she stayed on in the Pentre for several more years. We had asked Ethel more than enough, so we arranged with the pub at Mortimer's Cross to provide three mid-day meals in covered dishes which we collected for ourselves as well as for Henry. We managed like this for six months and never broke a dish; but we were thankful when the burden was lifted after the sale and Mary took over our cooking.

Our future was not yet determined. During the bad time with Ron we cheered ourselves on by planning the alterations and additions we might make to the Hill Farm house if we 'retired' up there; but to finance this we would need to sell Brook Bridge, and Frank Roberts' youngest son Edward had expressed interest in renting it. He and his fiancée Polly came to see us and we were happy at the thought of giving them a start; but they re-considered and we decided to sell.

In 1967 it was usual to sell farms by auction and we hardly considered a private sale, when we could have picked our customer: it was a bitterly regretted mistake. It did not occur to us that the farm, with its ideal milking set-up and beautiful grass leys, would be wanted for any other purpose than dairying. We were very naive, or perhaps past coherent thought: all our energy was concentrated on producing the farm and the herd in the best possible light. Much work went into the preparation of sale particulars and a careful catalogue of the cows: Geoffrey Chambers and Terry Court, for the auctioneers Russell, Baldwin and Bright, took immense trouble and between us we did a good job: the farm sale was planned for July and the herd sale for October in the hope that the incomer would be in a position to buy most of the cows and go straight ahead.

Of the many and varied folk we showed round the place David and Anne Thomas, a young couple looking for their first farm, were the ones we hoped for most. With hindsight we should have accepted their offer and cancelled the auction, but disinclination to run back on arrangements and disappoint other would-be bidders stopped us: throughout we had seen no sign of the successful customer or he would have had no chance.

On Friday July 28th 1967 a company gathered at the Royal Oak Hotel Leominster and Geoffrey Chambers offered Brook Bridge for sale: 'a beautiful little dairy farm set in the richest of Herefordshire soil'... and so on. It was knocked down at £15,750 to the huge poultry complex Sun Valley. We were shattered: we knew that soon our clover would be buried by concrete and rows of vast turkey houses would range across the fields and so it was. We have never forgiven ourselves for failing to protect that land.

The sale of the cows was a triumphant occasion because everyone was so nice. The cows were drawn quietly from their building by Mary and Henry into a ring at the Orchard gate, to be received by me, with Arthur behind me to loose them on into the Orchard as they were sold. Mary followed each one into the ring, so there we were together, with Terry Court at his cheerful best in the rostrum and merry remarks flying to and fro: 'Oh, here's a beauty' — 'One of the best now, Terry' — 'Look at her bag — there's some milk for you.' On it went through the forty odd herd, with Mary leading round the good little bull to finish. Every animal but one made more — some a lot more — than we had given for them, with three years milk and calves in between. It was a great investment financially and set us right for the future; but it had cost us too much personally. We were lucky to get out as well as we did.

153

Sheila and Mary at the Royal Show, 1969

XI
Interim

While we were clearing and cleaning the Brook Bridge house and buildings, ready to give possession on the appointed date, we watched Sun Valley's customers stripping out the milking machinery which had been sold, with our permission, at the end of our sale. A huge hole was knocked in the dairy wall to extract the bulk tank, which we had installed without such drastic action. We did not wait to see our beloved building filled with crates and turkey rubbish, nor did we watch the arrival of the earth movers, nor the falling of trees and grubbing of hedgerows. We kept ourselves down on Brook Farm, got on with the shepherding, tried to plan for the future and thanked heaven for another astounding stroke of good fortune.

Within a fortnight of our dispersal sale the first cases of the 1967 foot and mouth disease outbreak were announced near Shrewsbury. We were within the wide stand-still radius where all animal movement was banned, all sales and markets cancelled. We would have had to continue milking, but Henry would have gone. Instead of selling the many calves due in autumn we would have had to rear them ourselves, with no room, no routine, no labour. The work would have been insuperable: we could not believe our luck. The feeling of doom came later. We needed a holiday badly and planned a few days at St. David's.

During the time when we could not get away together Margaret and Alan had given us a wonderful annual break at Leintwardine: we went separately for two nights and a whole day in bed on River Lawn.

Mary's father had built a sleeping-out hut on the banks of the Teme, where she spent much time in childhood. Now Margaret tended occasional guests there, bringing meals on a tray while we lay reading, resting and listening to the river which ran by at our feet: in drought it receded, leaving an area of rushes below the lawn; but in flood it broke its banks and water crept up within a few feet of the hut, but never came in. The secluded garden lay between house and hut and we each wandered there in pyjamas; then back to bed and the book which seemed always special on River Lawn (my most magic one was Elizabeth Goudge's 'Little White Horse'.) The whole place was magic and is now a treasured memory; the only snag was that we were not there together.

After my legacy we managed sometimes a mid-week break in late autumn, when sheep sales were over. We ranged widely: three nights luxury at the Compleat Angler at Marlow, with kingfishers flashing down the Thames as we sat at breakfast; Budock Vean, near Falmouth, with the long dank hotel garden running down to the cove, where our blind Flirt, trusting us, paddled and climbed rocks; York, with the Minster and Bootham School and a horrible caravan drive home; and in 1960 an unforgettable week in Bavaria, staying with Else and Erich von Loeffelholz and their young family at Schottenstein, near Nuremberg. Our room was in one of the castle turrets, reached by a circular stair; it looked down on the tops of tall trees where red squirrels played, and out across a far wide valley, so that we felt alone on top of the world. By day we walked the district and talked (with no German!) to friendly farmers ploughing their fields with oxen. We were driven around the amazingly re-built Nuremberg and caught fish for supper from a monastery pool near Coburg, returning always to the laughter and happiness of a family who had suffered deeply in the post-war privation of Germany. We are close to them still.

We went first together to St. David's in 1952, when the Royal at Newton Abbot was in a foot and mouth disease area and sheep and cattle were banned. We were deeply disappointed: we had just taken delivery of the lorry and longed to try it, so Veronica invited us to St. Justinian's, to sleep in the lorry on the cliff's edge and to join the house party of children by day. Veronica's mother, Mrs. Whitehead, owned Ramsey Island and also the large mainland bungalow by the lifeboat slip which faces the Island across the Sound. There are two houses on the Island—the farm house, where Bertie Griffiths lived and farmed as the Whitehead's tenant; and a small bungalow further north, to which Mrs. Whitehead would retire, sometimes with a grandchild (great competition here!) when she needed rest from the family noise. Here she could be marooned for several days if the weather turned sour, as only small boats could make the Island landing place and these could not live in the Sound in a savage sea. Several of us were taken across one fine morning, the wind changed and by afternoon the waves seemed mountainous. The return crossing was rough, though even I, the poorest of sailors, made it all right, being absorbed by the seamanship of the life boat coxwain, Skipper Williams, whose fishing boat Mrs. Whitehead employed when she could. It was a marvellous experience, and a very happy holiday.

Fourteen years on we came again to St. David's each November for three years running in the bad time of the dairy herd; in between, we thought of the seals when we could not sleep. We stayed in an hotel but based the van at St. Justinian's by day. We walked south for miles on the cliff path and saw not a soul: a pair of black crow-like birds with red beaks and legs, flapped ahead of us. (At home we were laughed at by Margaret and Alan for not recognising them as choughs.) We lay for hours on our tummies, the Indian summer sun warming our backs, and looked down into the clear green depths of the sea. Off shore two dark heads bobbed up and watched; then a form detached itself and swam in. The seal hauled out onto the rocks and pulled herself heavily upwards to her white pup, who lay waiting above high water mark. She suckled him, and when he nipped her she beat him heartily with a heavy flipper. He finished and lay content while she groomed him vigorously with the same flipper. Then she left him, lumbered down the rocks, slid into the water and swam to join her watching mate. They danced in ecstasy, twisting and turning as they dived together into the deep: they coupled, parted, coupled again, dived deeper, every movement of their writhing bodies clear to us through the green water. Then they surfaced, looked back to the shore and swam seawards together, she to return on the next tide to suckle her pup once more.

Further south, near Carn-ar-Wig, the cliff lowers towards the shore and we were able to get down and climb out on a rocky promontory, with deep water lapping our feet. Fifty yards beyond us a huge bull seal lay basking in the sun on a large rock, surrounded by five or six lounging females. They looked at us with curiosity, unafraid; then two of the young cows slipped into the water and swam towards us. Mary sang to them ('Over the Seas to Skye'!) and they came closer, almost to our feet, not quite to our outstretched hands, listening and looking for many minutes before they swam back to rejoin their lord. We returned to St. Justinian's in a dream and sat eating in the van in wonder and contentment, while the Island lay like a dark whale against the sunset, with the sea creaming over the cruel Bitches rocks on its flank.

Early November is the peak of the breeding season for the Atlantic seal: vulnerable white pups lie dotted round the coast, some approachable by boat in calm weather. One morning on the steps down to the lifeboat jetty we met a young fellow bumping up a bulging bag. We helped to ease its occupant, and queried the contents: he was taking a seal pup to Bristol University 'for a couple of days' for research ('we have a pool'.) 'What happens next?' we asked. 'Oh, we bring him back to the same rock and his mother will come back to him.' We wondered... We wondered too what use a pool would be to a pup who couldn't swim, and what would happen to the returning boat if the weather were rough. Such behaviour would not have been tolerated in Mrs. Whitehead's day; but she had sold the Island.

We watched the Island boat tie up at the jetty: the new tenants, Mr. and Mrs. Allison, came ashore with seventy dead rabbits for sale.

We introduced ourselves and after some general farming chat they invited us across to the Island.

They collected us on a fine warm morning: the crossing was calm and as we edged into the little landing place we were watched by a bull seal, hauled out on a rock in the sun. We climbed the steep path from harbour to house and sat in the garden, with the sea at our feet, drinking tea and talking too long for the tide, which needed to be low for our visit to Seal Cave. We walked across to the Atlantic side of the Island, slithered down the crumbly cliff face, jumped a rock gulley up which the sea was washing already and plunged into the semi-darkness of the cave. As we came, so went about half a dozen seal cows, making a terrific clatter as they crashed past us, lumbering over the rocky floor until they slid into the safety of deep sea at the cave mouth. Behind them they left a crowd of pups, lying in groups at the back of the cave: there were far more pups than the mums who fled—some looked sickly and two were dead. Overcrowding in seal sanctuaries is a problem: the pups develop an intestinal infection which scours them, like calves in a crowded pen. Many die—no doubt the tough ones live, a form of natural selection, but the farmer's instinct to preserve made us unhappy at the sight of the sick pups, and we could do nothing to help. Anyway we had to get out: the sea was washing in fast and the gulley jump, our only retreat, was hazardous. We all got wet and I landed waist deep in water, ruining my good cord trousers, though I have them still— my 'sea trousers'. The climb back up the cliff was stiff; the face crumbled under feet and hands and we brought home several small pieces of shining quartz. The sun warmed and dried us as we sat again in the Allisons' garden, eating a late sandwich lunch laced with delicious elderflower wine, made by Mrs. Allison on the Island. At last we tore ourselves away and were landed at St. Justinian's on the high tide, feeling as if we had come from another world.

We returned home in 1967 to find that foot and mouth disease was spreading steadily: on November 16th the whole country was closed for animal movement—no sales, no markets, no racing, no hunting; a licence was necessary to move stock across a public road to another field on one's own farm, so that we could not graze the Brook meadows.

Two days before Christmas I was delivering gifts to friends on Bircher Common and stepped out of the van within feet of some sheep on the road: next morning, with the milk, came news that foot and mouth was confirmed on the Common. We were aghast. Bircher Common belongs to the National Trust and is less than two miles as the crow flies from Hill Farm, three miles from the Brook. Over Christmas all the Commoners' stock was rounded up, the sheep and cattle slaughtered and burnt, ponies impounded and as many as possible of the wild fallow deer tracked down through the forest and shot; but many must have escaped to spread the infection to further farms. The misery and anxiety hung over us all.

We shut ourselves up as completely as we could. The van tyres were scrubbed with disinfectant and I discarded the boots I wore on the Common. We allowed no vehicles in and received our goods and Christmas gifts over the garden gate; anyone who had to come in must walk through a bath of disinfectant. We did not go to Leintwardine as usual on Christmas Day, but stayed quietly together and Mary experimented with the Kenwood mixer I had given her. Another consolation was plenty of time to work on our plans for the extension we hoped to build on to the house at Hill Farm.

Weeks went by, the sheep and cattle were well and we began to breathe again. We talked often on the telephone to Barbara Turner, who was on her own at Ashley Moor, the other side of the Common. She was terrified for her pedigree Herefords and kept them in, with gauze over the doors and windows. At her suggestion and without much faith we hung halved onions on the trees around Brook Farm—these were supposed to trap the air-borne germs! Whether or not they did, we escaped the dreaded doom of slaughter and burning and at midnight on January 27th '68 our area was de-restricted, though the dying disease cropped up sporadically through the country until March, when everywhere was clear. There has been no epidemic in the U.K. since—a vindication of the slaughter policy and the restriction of imported meat from the Argentine.

As soon as we were free to move about again we went up to Lucton to discuss with Arthur and Mrs. Duggan our re-possession of Hill Farm in 1970. We had decided that the time had come to sell up at the Brook and 'retire'. The thought of living in peace on top of the hill, surrounded by glorious countryside and far from the traffic and depradations of Sun Valley, seemed too good to be true; but would the Duggans agree to move down? We offered them the Woodhouse cottage and its little orchard at a modest rent and the nine acres of the Brook meadows rent-free for three years, when Arthur would get his pension. After much thought they decided to accept and we all signed an informal agreement. We heard a sheep sale rumour later on that we should not get possession after all, but they were as good as their word; in the end poor Arthur was glad to go down nearer his sons and their families, for Mrs. Duggan died tragically during an operation. It was a hard time for him but he held on. He preferred to buy the Woodhouse rather than rent it, and this we were able to arrange. He made a good go of things and continued for years to help us after we had all made the move.

In the early days as we picked potatoes or turned hay on Hill Farm, with the valley spread below us and the Black Mountains in the west, we said often 'Of course this is where we should live'; but we never considered it seriously then. Now the electricity had come up, and the telephone, and after about ten years' hard work on the Hereford Water Board we achieved mains water in 1967. Arthur had struggled for fourteen years with the inadequate borehole and windmill, and one of the small houses down the Lane depended entirely on stored rainwater. Our water troubles were not over with the arrival of the mains, but it was a triumph to get it up at last. We put in a downstairs bathroom and loo for the Duggans as soon as we could.

We were in touch again with our good builders, Ernest Deacon and Sons of Kington. We asked Arthur Deacon to consider whether our plans for the Hill Farm extension were feasible or whether we should need an architect: we wondered whether the structure would carry the number of windows we wanted. We planned a gabled extension at right angles to the little old house—one large ground floor room (26 x 16 feet) with double glazed windows in each wall and a French window into the imagined garden on the south. Above, two rooms, a bedroom like the bridge of a ship, commanding the magnificent view of the mountains, with twelve opening windows to south, east and west; and a larger dressing room with two very large walk-in clothes cupboards. There were to be four small gables, three south and one north, with wide-opening double windows let into the roof of the old house.

'Mr. Arthur' thought we could manage without an architect and produced a set of splendid plans and an elastic estimate: we expected to have comfortable capital after the sale of Brook Farm. We had fun with the plans through the rest of the winter, looked and measured on site in the spring, and arranged firmly with 'Mr. Arthur' to build through the summer of 1970. He promised to start in early April and finish in September: his men began work on April 6th and the last one left on September 9th! Such is the service we have always had from Deacons.

For two years we carried on at Brook Farm, buying and selling store cattle and showing the sheep as usual, though the gilt was off the gingerbread. Whenever we could we escaped up to Lucton, walked or rode in the woods, or helped Arthur, with seeds, fertiliser and some tractor driving, to lay down to grass his small patches of tillage. He removed his wire dividing fences until we were left with three sizeable meadows and some smaller paddocks ready for grazing when we took over.

We concluded our sheep showing with a good season in 1969, when our two year old stock ram Baynham Joseph, was first and reserve champion at the Royal, and champion at our last 'local', Tenbury, always a favourite and happy show for us. Little did we think then that we should be back there with ponies in a few years' time!

The building starts at Hill Farm, April 1970

The spring of 1970 was late and cold, with snow and frost on into April. Lambing was rough (there is a diary entry in Mary's writing on March 16th: 'Oh so tired—both have aching feet') and clouded by the realisation that there was no on-going—the whole flock would soon be gone for good. But on March 24th another diary entry says: 'Arthur Deacon rang about the staircase at Hill Farm— makes it feel very close now'; and below, in my writing: 'Beginning to see daylight.' And so we moved on into that incredibly busy summer.

The house building was our first priority: each working day one of us went up to Lucton to meet the men, to answer their questions, to agree minor alterations or to make snap decisions. I found that my brain could carry details clearly—I could visualize such things as pipe depths and junctions even when not on site, and so we avoided some mistakes—of course we made some, but not many, and it was a pleasure to work with men who were so keenly interested in the

163

job. Even our request for no radio music was honoured, a courtesy we have always received from Deacon's men.

At Brook Farm we plodded on with our routine work and tidied and gardened intensively, to have the place looking at its best before the auction sale in early June. In spite of the Brook Bridge lesson we decided to sell by auction because we needed firm dates for cash and completion—we could not face dragging negotiations with private customers. We thought that there was little chance of housing development being allowed on the land as it lies outside the planned boundaries of Kingsland village; and we hoped that the small grass fields and tidy hedges would attract a retiring farmer who would be unlikely to plough and grub up. With this in mind we offered the house and buildings with 17 acres in one lot, and three outlying fields separately, so that neighbours could have a go. The strategy worked, though at no great prices and Lot 1 fell to a retired gentleman from 'up the country' for £12,000. He did not stay long and the buildings deteriorated: the Canadian maples and line of silver birches we planted in the roadside hedge were quickly felled, and we arrived along the road one day just as the white cherry at the garden gate was cut to the ground in its prime. Since we left, Brook Farm has changed hands three or four times, and the orchard has been grubbed up: we grieve still for the towering pear tree with its mantle of white blossom and its massive harvest of perry pears which brought us much profit from Bulmers. But the lovely land is still there, a new cattle building has improved the farm, and we understand that the price has gone up by leaps and bounds.

Showing round prospective buyers took a lot of time in May, though it was pleasant, with the place looking so well and many nice people appreciating it; but we were glad to get that hurdle over and turn our attention to preparations for the 'live and dead stock' sale in September. ('Dead stock' comprises all inanimate farming objects and would include many of our treasured possessions such as the pony float and our beloved lorry.) We decided to keep the van for a while, to help us through the move, but we ordered a new blue

164

Brook Farm dispersal sale, 1970

Landrover with a 'de luxe' cab costing £1,035 in those days, and a new 'Farmers Hunt' Rice trailer to match, at £315. These were delivered before the sale, in September 1970, so we did not feel too bereft of transport.

The catalogue preparation entailed much work. The ewes and ewe lambs were listed in pens of five, with pedigrees included; the rams and ram lambs were sold singly. All the 'dead stock', down to the last 'two buckets and a shovel', were catalogued in separate lots and set out in long lines in the meadow, with plenty of space between each lot.

We were helped immensely in this work by our neighbour, the Cross family of Lower Cross Farm, Hereford Lane: Mr. Cross senior, kindly and quiet; his son Ernie, cheerful and full of work; and young David, hand in hand with grandad until they got specially busy with the fold units, which had to be set out just right for the small boy. His two brothers were at school, but Andrew the eldest used to help us scout bob-a-jobbing from time to time. He is now in partnership with his father and Lower Cross has grown from thirty-five to eighty-five acres with the purchase of land in the Covernhope valley. They allowed us to buy from them our little 'Connop Meadow' at the top, which they now hold as our tenants. They are a wonderful family, a shining example of how a small mixed farm can be made viable by sheer hard work. When Mr. Cross retired we used to swop books with him—he was a great reader. He left behind him a farming family with whom we are proud to be friends.

In the midst of our cataloguing Brian and Helen (Mary's nephew and godson and his fiancée, Helen Longmore) announced their wedding for a fortnight before our sale. We thought that we could not make it, but of course we did and it was a memorable day. The service at Condover Church was moving, their love shone out, and when they went to sign the register a young school-girl stepped into the aisle and sang 'The Lord is my Shepherd' in a voice which rose to heaven. She was Janie Vyvyan-Robinson: we shall remember her always.

Our sale day came and was fine, but prices were poor. The cattle trade had slumped and some nice little Hereford bullocks we bought in the spring were sold at a loss. The sheep made little more than commercial price: upland breeders never like to buy from the valley and our flock was thought to be too 'clean' for the new dark fashion. We were grieved especially over one outstanding show ewe lamb: we put her in the best pen which was knocked down at an ordinary price, and a breeder drew her out afterwards, giving the buyer a profit to sell her singly. We thought he could have bid on for the pen.

By the end we were too tired to think straight at all; but the next day we went up to Lucton and the future looked good.

XII
'Retirement'

By early October the house was ready for our move. Pamela had cleaned it from top to toe, the carpet was laid, the curtains in the new part professionally hung. The grey-green carpet runs throughout, except for kitchen, hall and workroom—we were not used to carpeted stairs or bath room, and Frances said every mark would show. (After nineteen years there are very few!) The rightness of the sitting room curtains amazes us—we found the material within a week of deciding on the carpet; the greens match perfectly and the magnolia pattern picks up the colour of the mellow tiled window sills. We wonder nowadays that we dared to afford such a wealth of material, but the joy of the room has repaid us a hundred fold.

We moved the furniture ourselves, using Land Rover, trailer and van, helped only with the few heavy things by Arthur and a kind neighbour at the Brook. We had built the sitting room wall spaces to take the two dressers and my desk and they look good—they could not be seen properly in the small rooms at Brook Farm. The new Aga and sink units fit well in the old kitchen, with its heavy beams, and an extra double-glazed window on the north makes the room very light. Words fail me about our bedroom, with its wealth of windows: it fills our dreams.

We decided to sleep first at Hill Farm on October 17th, bringing cats and bitches up with us at evening feed time. We can't remember how many cats we had to move, there were always a lot. (The peak, in the dairy days of two farmyards, was 16.) Our original stock stemmed from the six-toed Meesch, though she did not pass on that trait; but after some years at Brook Farm we had a dreadful epidemic of cat 'flu and lost the lot. We waited some time before restocking, then started again with a splendid she called Julia, a real farmyard cat. She was a washy tortoishell, grey, orange and white, but her rare tortoishell kittens were the true rich colour and we never put one down. As tortoishells are always female (we have never heard of a male) our stock multiplied; and there were other reasons for keeping kittens. We had a rule that each female should rear one a season, if possible a ginger tom, for which there was a steady demand, as also for ginger shes, but these are very rare (strange that sex should dominate colour in these few cases.) It was easier in those days to find homes for kittens, but promises could fail and then we were landed with an extra, as we could not bring ourselves to put down reared kittens. We tried always to take the babies from mum at twenty-four hours old—a sickening job which we shared. We killed swiftly by striking the head hard on a paving stone—(*never* by drowning, a horribly slow, cruel method, though it may be easier for the operator). The slain kittens were buried quickly in the near-by mixon, and we tried hard not to let the mums know what had happened. Their continuing joy with what remained was a recompense for us.

We planned the cat move carefully. On the evening of the 17th we called them to feed as usual and when they came we gathered them up in pairs and fastened them safely into boxes and baskets waiting in the van. But one cat was missing—the White Knight, a great character and mighty hunter who was often absent from meals. We could not wait for him, so bundled the three bitches, Bunty, Trudy and Tess, into the front with us and set off on that momentous journey; but as we passed the Brook Meadows a white figure emerged and strode down the middle of the road towards us, tail erect in salute. Mary scooped him up onto her lap and he rode proud to his new hunting grounds. We drove on in triumph and as we crossed the

River Lugg bridge a kingfisher flashed across our bows, an omen of the joys to come.

We woke next morning in a transport of happiness, a dream come true. The diary says, in Mary's writing: 'Heavenly morning—wonderful waking in that glorious place!' We soon came down to earth again, but it was one of those rare times with which we are blessed in life.

1970 was a heavy fruit year and we had orchards to harvest on both places, as we did not give possession of Brook Farm until mid-November. We would bring a load of furniture in the morning and spend the rest of the day picking up apples at Hill Farm while Arthur and other helpers, including Pamela and her girls, picked up at the Brook. Each week we hauled ridiculously heavy loads to Bulmers, up to two and a half tons in the trailer, with another half ton in the Land Rover, making the steering very dicey. Our total that year was about nineteen tons. We had to leave a lot of fruit at Brook Farm but the loads from the Hill continued until nearly Christmas. We were thankful to finish and turn our attention to making the garden.

The house stood, stark in its shining white rough-cast, on a plateau of builders' rubble which was covered with a generous layer of rich farmyard top soil, swept by the JCB from the building site and barn. The ground sloped steeply down from the old garden to a tiny paddock, used heavily by Arthur at lambing and sheep gathering times. We pulled up the dividing fence, ploughed the little paddock (a fiddly job, beautifully done for us by our Mortimer's Cross neighbour, Martin Raymond) and in 1971 it grew a fine crop of potatoes, while we laid the 'plateau' down to grass and started to clothe the house with climbers. The concrete surrounding path was laced with pockets of earth and everything planted against the house grew mightily; a cotoneaster horizontalis, which now hosts a myriad bees in blossom time and whose scarlet berries feast our large family of blackbirds well into the winter; a japonica which grew vastly up and outwards across the path and on to the lawn—only lately have I persuaded Mary to cut it back to the ground; and a ceanothus, whose dusty-blue blossoms were a joy against the white wall. It became a great tree, strong enough to support our neighbour's peacock, who flew with raucous shrieks, up to my bedroom window early one Sunday morning. (Mary caught him from below and popped him in a barrel until she was ready to carry him home down the Lane.) Alas! the ceanothus did not survive the fierce winter of 1981-82; neither did the passion flower which rioted with a honeysuckle beside the garden door: we marvelled at its exquisite clock-face blooms and miss it greatly. But we still have the clump of iris stylosa on the east side of the door, another flowering miracle with its visibly opening mid-winter buds. We persuaded thymes and other low creepers across the concrete path and in a year or so the place looked clothed.

Hill Farm, 1976

There are two gnarled old apple trees, a Beauty of Bath and a Bramley, on the Lane side of the garden (clumps of pink and white cyclamen now flourish under them) but otherwise the place was bare of trees and shrubs and we set about planting—with hindsight perhaps too much, but we and the creatures love it. Lilacs, buddleias and a viburnum fragrans run down the Lane hedge; a tiny acacia set in the wild bit near the bottom fence has become a thirty foot tree, soaring and graceful, while the sycamore shoots which we allowed to grow up in the west hedge are taller, a massive clump which shades the vegetables overmuch. A magnolia, set in the middle just above the wild bit, is protected from the north by a guelder rose—both bushes bring a wealth of white blooms, but the guelder rose shields the magnolia from sight of the house. A staghorn sumach, planted where the west hedge joins the Paddock rails, blocks part of the flower garden from view of the sitting room windows, but its glory of autumn gold must be enjoyed while possible, for it is sinking and when it lands on the lawn it must go; but it has a healthy child under its skirts. Our most short-sighted but best loved planting was a little prunus autumnalis hard by the house: it has grown into the Magic Tree, whose branches almost touched the bedroom windows until firmly reduced. Its winter wealth of tiny pink blossom is attacked ruthlessly by the tits which swarm in the branches en route for the bird table, high out of reach of leaping cats. (I have to service the table from steps—Mary can just reach.) The blackbirds use the tree as an easy stepping stone to our bedroom window sill, which is spread daily in winter with pinhead oatmeal and is entirely safe from cats. Robins, tits and chaffinches feed here too, and in summer wrens run along the top of the open windows, gleaning flies from inside. A spotted woodpecker and nuthatches come often to the table and we have had a jay; but all the birds are fewer than they used to be.

Our most triumphant planting was the wistaria which now almost covers two faces of the Dutch barn and has reached the roof. It was slow to start until we found that it needed copious watering throughout the year; then it ramped and its training is Mary's magnum opus.

She led the shoots along bamboos fastened horizontally between the heads of the cladding nails, so that now the ugly expanses of corrugated iron are almost hidden by pendant blossoms and feathery green leaves. The high ladder work was nerve-wracking for me, standing on the bottom rung. I wonder who will climb one day to pull down the wistaria because it may ruin the roof.

The seeding of the lawns was a laborious job, running over two springs. The top half, in '71, came down to a good tilth after endless raking and rolling: then we lined out the ground in squares, measured the good quality lawn seed and sowed it on our hands and knees — it took ages, but we were lucky with the weather and got a good sward. After the potatoes and a winter to settle, the lower half did not need nearly so much working. In its middle we marked out a rectangular vegetable patch leading up into a kidney shaped flower border which Mary cut in glorious curves: filled with roses, shrubs, and herbaceous plants it carries colour through the season and the fight with ground elder is worth winning. The whole patch is surrounded by grass, laid down in '72 and mown in winding paths round trees and bushes leading into the bottom wild. Snowdrops and daffodils surround the garden, which looks bigger than it is — it can't be more than half an acre. We love it dearly.

We love too the banky grass fields, surrounded on three sides by the woods: from the top the view is breath-taking. On the south the mellow red-tiled house roof shows through the shade of the orchard trees; south-west stretches rolling countryside, fields, woods and low hills, tillage and grass, reaching away to the Black Mountains. Why black, we wonder? They look pearly from here. On a clear day Mynydd Troed and the Brecon Beacons stand out beyond. We can view all this from the west windows of the house too — what a place in which to live!

We had given little thought to stocking our fields — the winter was before us and grass keep is easy to sell in spring. But rather foolishly we had kept six ewes and needed a ram for them, so when a local farmer offered to send up a bunch of his Kerry Hill ewes and a tup, to run with ours, we accepted gladly. For some years after this he sent us sheep and cattle through the summer. We managed them round the ponies and charged per head per week. This meant a lot of booking for us, and his way with stock was not ours. We parted company after he sent us a bunch of freshly docked ewes: blood dripped from the sad stumps as they were driven up the Lane, and in a few days many of the wounds were writhing with maggots. We struggled to dress them but had to give up in despair, and asked him to fetch the ewes home. Next day he came in a rage and removed the rest of his stock: it was a horrid episode, but it led to a lasting association which has brought us great happiness.

Tentatively we offered the keep to our old friend Verney Pugh and his son Colin who farm at Cwmwhitton, on the Welsh border above Knighton, fifteen miles from here. We did not think that they would want to come so far with stock, but they did, and are still coming. We had known Verney and his father for many years, showing and selling sheep together and visiting each other's farms. Colin as a very small boy came once to Brook Farm and gazed, fascinated, at our cart, which was fitted at the time with an 'iron horse', a tractor hitch between the shafts. On the way home he asked: 'Dad, what was that trailer with two sticks on it?' He had never seen a horse-drawn cart before.

Verney is a large wise man with quiet dignity, at home in a London conference room, escorting royalty round a show, driving a tractor or calving a cow. He has the O.B.E for his services to farming and is a J.P. in the county of Powys. Colin is the cream of young farmers, a leader of Welsh Young Farmers' Clubs, with a talent for modern machinery and an organising flair. Together they have made Cwmwhitton one of the finest farms in the country: the Prime Minister has been to see it as the model of an 'improved hill farm'. We are wonderfully lucky to have their stock.

We sell the grass keep to them by the acre, April to November, with the right to manage the grazing as we think fit. At first we reserved some acres, but now that our ponies have gone, and with the Hill Croft ground, we can offer the full forty acres: on this we can carry for the season up to thirty cattle and a hundred dry sheep. The cattle are beautiful Welsh Black heifers, some in calf, some younger: they thrive here and are a joy to watch. The sheep are yearling ewes, a few Kerries but mostly Welsh Mules (Blue-faced Leicester ram on Welsh ewe) which we find hard to like, with their washy face markings and slack coats, though we are assured that with a Down ram they bring the strong lean lamb the butcher wants.

All the stock here are seen daily, without fail—twice a day when we are both fit and to ensure that Jane has enough exercise. She is not allowed near the cattle and wisely keeps her distance, with an eye always on us. Round the sheep she is good and steady, and holds them for us lightly, so that we can look them over really well—I don't know what we would do without her. We never attempt to catch sheep these days, but it goes against the grain to see lame sheep and not to treat them. In an emergency Verney or Colin is here like a shot, and when we report that treatment is needed they always respond; but we don't expect them to come specially for odd foot dressings and here we feel our shepherding falls short. Indeed all our farming now, except the poultry enterprise, is below our former standard: the bigger fields are harrowed in spring and topped in late summer—too late usually to stop the thistles seeding. They receive dressings of lime, phosphate or potash—never nitrogen—as the occasional soil test indicates or our combined knowledge tells. Our 'gaffers' do all this for us, but there are places which their large machinery cannot reach and we leave the small paddocks untreated as an experiment, though we keep them heavily grazed. We cherish the rough places, especially at Hill Croft, and manage the farm as a nature reserve as far as we can; and although it feels odd to us not to have total command of the stock it is accepted that on our own place we are boss, and for this we are grateful.

XIII
Hill Croft

Hill Croft is a lovely little smallholding of nearly eight acres, whose land, on the east side of Lucton Lane, marches opposite Hill Farm from the archway to the forest gates. Its cottage lies just below the level of our garden fence, on the opposite side of the Lane. From here, no doubt, the shepherd or wood man walked through School Wood to his work at Croft Castle, for surely all four of the cottages up the east side of the Lane, each with its bit of land, were occupied in the old days by the Crofts' work folk. There was a fifth dwelling too, the lodge whence the gate-keeper ran to open up for the carriages passing over the archway. This is marked now by scattered stone and a carpet of snowdrops at the bottom of Hill Croft ground, but when we became interested there was a flimsy chalet-type dwelling in place, and talk of a building plot to be sold off. On the north meadow, opposite the Hill Farm entrance gate, was a dwelling caravan, with a right of way on to the Lane: possible purchasers were viewing this delectable building site. We needed to secure Hill Croft.

We asked the elderly lady who lived there with her daughter whether we might have first refusal should she ever wish to sell. This was promised, but she died in 1968 and the daughter wanted such an exorbitant price that we decided to let it go to auction. We spoke to the auctioneers, who were acting for us as well as for the vendors, and on May 17th we drove to Leominster with butterflies in our tummies. Knowing looks greeted us as we passed through the hotel bar to the sale room, where we were eyed by the sprinkling of people present: a few curious neighbours, a local farmer and two strangers.

The auctioneer spoke his preamble ('charming little place, just right for retirement, keep a horse or two, hunting and shooting in unspoilt countryside, what could be nicer...') and we sat in growing tension until at last he called for bids: 'I ought to ask you £12,000 — no? Well ten, then — oh! come along, ladies and gentlemen, a beautiful little property like this...' No-one stirred, and on he went down the scale until I called out '£4,000'. 'Thank you, madam — £4,000 I'm bid — £4,500 — £5,000...' One of the strangers had a go, the local farmers tipped a wink or two and so did I; but at £6,500 I stopped, shaking my head to leave no doubt that our limit was reached. The auctioneer bid on a bit, but everyone must have thought it was against the reserve and at £7,000 the property was withdrawn. We too withdrew, to a corner of the hotel lounge, and the auctioneer popped in and out between us and unseen parties until he told us that it would be ours at £7,250. Our plan had worked: we signed the contract and a happy buy was sealed.

However, negotiations were not fully over: the archway plot had been sold off to the chalet dweller, who spoke darkly of building a permanent home: we worked hard for many months until we persuaded him to sell to us at £1,000. We then sold off the chalet and an additional caravan and closed the rough entrance into the Lane. The snowdrops spread across the drive and an unspoilt Hill Croft was ours.

With the help of contractors we levelled and worked the chalet site, grubbed up the inferior apple trees, laid drains below to carry off the surplus spring water which ran down from the woods, broadcast by hand a balanced fertiliser, and Arthur fiddled on a permanent grass seed mixture. A seed fiddle is a small canvas bag hung in a light wooden frame; the seed falls from the bag into a box below, whence it is spun out by a metal spinner; this is rotated by a leather thong attached to a bow. The sower walks to and fro across the field between marks, with the fiddle slung on his front by a strap across the shoulder: with his stride he rhythmically works the bow and the seed is spun out in even waves on either side. Arthur is a wizard

Hill Croft in 1970 before we did anything

fiddler and has sown many acres for us in his time. We have the
fiddle still.

When we bought Hill Croft the seven and a half acres of rough
grass land was divided into six plots; but the untended old hedges
were gone in the bottom and animals could wander the whole place
at will. We decided on two plots, Top and Bottom, with a single water
trough between: we gapped up the centre hedge with posts and rails
but left all the old hedgerows, with their gnarled damson and apple
trees and their high hazel and blackthorn bushes, so that whichever
way the wind is blowing there is always shelter. Three sides of the
whole place are girt by the woods, so that it is snug in winter and full
of deep shade in summer—the comfort of cattle, under the
magnificent hornbeams on the south, is a joy to see.

Only one field is named in the deeds, the Cricket Pitch, a straight
strip running east towards the Castle: we imagine the men and boys
playing there on summer evenings while their women folk watch

177

from the bank where the snowdrops bloom in spring. We have named the other five divisions after the dwellings of my youth: The Lickey, Fox Lydiatt, Gorse Bank, Beechcroft and The Holte. The Lickey, where my grandfather lived, was the old Rose and Crown Inn, the first coaching stage on the Birmingham to Bristol run. Here I 'helped' the cowman, Smallwood, lay paths up the hills, with Edward the donkey hauling gravel in a little cart. The place was bought afterwards by one of the Cadbury family, who gave it to Birmingham Corporation: now the public can stroll on those paths and enjoy the chain of duck pools dropping down the hillside. Fox Lydiatt was the home of a beloved maid, Gorse Bank the cottage opposite the Lickey gates where I was born. Beech Croft was the house in Barnt Green whence Nanny would walk us, my sister Prue in the pram, to the top of the Lickey Hill, there often to meet (it seemed by chance) 'Tommy Tester', in his greasy overalls, testing the new Austin 20, that extraordinary looking tourer whose hood was submerged in its rounded back. Tommy roared up the hill with great frequency from the fast growing Austin works at Longbridge, in the valley near Redditch. The Holte, much later, was the house by the golf links in Harborne, Birmingham, where my mother died.

None of the fields were stocked when we bought Hill Croft except the Holte, where we found Pud, a golden dun cob 'on tack' from our neighbour Geoffrey Jackson, who had no field at Greenhaven, to which he and Barbara had just retired. We were glad to keep her on, and when we came up from the valley it was great to be greeted by a golden pony trotting to meet and talk. From time to time, for a treat, we accepted Geoffrey's offer to 'ride her whenever you like.' This was a delight—she walked on well and was a champion deer spotter: her flickering ears told where to watch, and she was a tireless stalker. We saw much in the woods that year; one day she stood motionless over a woodcock basking in the middle of the ride and then let it fly off under her nose; but you had to sit tight when deer broke across.

When we came up to live at Hill Farm Geoffrey let us buy Pud; he was not feeling fit, he knew he could ride her if he so wished, and none of us could bear to part with her. We bought her for £160 as a 'riding pony' guessing her to be a doubtful breeder but feeling sure that she was a pedigree Welsh Cob. Our breeder friends exclaimed when they saw her, and we were offered more than we gave for her, barren and 'without papers' as she was. We were short of riding time and it seemed a shame to let a splendid mare fail to breed; so in 1972, when she was twelve, we set to work.

Geoffrey traced her registration certificate and we were able to write to her breeder: Pud turned out to be Cefnlys Pertina, the first and last foal of her mother, who did not breed again. Pud had her own first foal as a three year old but did not hold again to service and was sold eventually to a pony trekking stable, from where Geoffrey bought her.

We decided to spare no effort in one really good try. In Spring 1973 our vet pronounced Pud right and straight: there was no obvious reason why she should not breed. In case difficult loadings or anxious travelling were factors to consider, we arranged with Clifford Rawlings for the smallest of his thoroughbred stallions, Clear Delivery, to travel up to her: there was a beautiful quiet service, repeated a few days later. At fifty-four days she was blood tested in foal and we spent a happy and hopeful winter; but by the spring it was obvious that no foal was there.

We had been to Sarah Featherstonehaugh's Trewysgoed Stud about a cob stallion for next time and fallen for the thirty year old Hendy Brenin, magnificent and looking half his age; and Sarah had been here and fallen for Pud. When the disappointment came she agreed readily to have Pud at Trewysgoed and try an implant. (A capsule of the hormone progesterone is implanted in the mare's neck after conception and removed immediately before she is due to foal.) Pud was served by Hendy Brenin in May 1973 and held at three and six weeks; but the implant was missed and she turned at nine weeks—she had lost the foal. By then it was too late to start again, but they were enjoying her as a ride so we all agreed on another try next year.

179

On May 10th 1974 Pud was served again by Hendy Brenin and held at six weeks. Progesterone was implanted on August 1st 1974 and removed on April 1st 1975. On Friday May 9th at 7.15 a.m. our telephone rang and Sarah's excited voice said: 'Pud had a filly foal, under my window at 6 o'clock and I said to Robert "My God it's in a bag" and flew in my nightdress.' What Pud thought of this apparition we don't know, but Sarah found her very possessive of a lovely dun filly and all was well.

In June we had the joy of seeing Pud and her foal gracing that fine herd of cobs on the mountainside, fulfilled at last. We decided to let her stay to bring them another foal or two if she would, before returning to end her days with us. She brought a colt in 1976 but that first filly was 'the one to remember': she was called Trewysgoed Proof (of the Pudding!)

Then sadness came: Sarah felt that she must reduce her stock and asked us to have Pud back there and then. We were exhausted, with far too much work and far too many ponies—we felt we couldn't cope. Sarah found her a good home and to our shame we sold her; but the 'good home' sold her on and we lost track of her. We were sad.

Then, out of the blue, in 1980, came a letter from Maureen Francis of Tyllys, Tretower: 'I thought you would like to know that Pud (Cefnlys Pertina) is still going strong...she is very much loved and a great family cob...and has been covered by the Welsh Champion Stallion "Cathedine Danny Boy" and so far has not turned, so we are hoping for a nice foal.' We hastened to tell about the probable need for an implant, but it was already too late. Maureen thought that Pud turned at nine weeks and wrote to us 'No foal next year'; but in Spring '81 Pud was found with Tyllys Surprise by her side, a dun filly, achieved without an implant. She was a beauty and Maureen was thrilled. In August we went to see them and came home with a lasting memory of two golden ponies grazing in a sunlit meadow, with a range of magnificent mountains behind. It was a very happy visit.

Pud did not have to face another winter. She was twenty-one now and had been very stiff with arthritis while carrying Surprise. One morning, after the foal was weaned she was found dead in her field—a heart attack it was thought. Her memory lives on for us at Hill Croft.

We did not need the Hill Croft house until we moved up to live at Hill Farm, when my cousins, Mary and Denis Mather and their three girls, would furnish and use it as a holiday cottage; but the underbidder approached us after the sale. He worked in Anglesey but had family ties in London and wanted a half-way house. We came to a pleasant agreement whereby he undertook to do all the electrical installation and use it for the spare two years. We would hasten to modernise it, and again we were lucky, as Deacons were at Hill Farm putting in a bathroom and loo for the Duggans, and were able to go straight on with Hill Croft.

The cottage was thin and narrow, two up, two down, with a steep tiled roof, once thatched, no doubt, and small low upper windows. We put in three gabled dormers and built on a porch to match. The walls were clad with a thin layer of new white rough cast, but a slab fell off just before the auction so we renewed the lot. It always seems a shame to cover the old daub and wattle, but the cladding was put on for a purpose and it would have been too expensive to weather proof the old walls in any other way. The cottage looked good when finished, a cub of the Hill Farm house.

When we replaced the dear old double pigscot, which was collapsing slowly into the field, we took care to have the new pigscot building in keeping with the rest of the place, using old tiles for the roof and 'wavy edge' elm boards for cladding. We did not need planning permission, as it replaced another agricultural building and was just over 80 feet from the road, but in courtesy we informed the District Council of our plans. This cost us £20 and a visit of inspection after we were well under way. Early one morning came a frantic telephone call from Deacons: 'The planners are objecting to the rough edge of the elm boards—they say it looks too rural. Shall we send down a circular saw and cut them straight?' I gulped and told them 'No—carry on building.' We heard no more!

After many happy holidays the Mathers moved to live and work in Cumbria and found the distance too great to come regularly to Hill Croft. We already had other guests in their absence, notably the 'Brumcrofts'—Ruth Waugh, my father's secretary, Pam Greenway, from Birmingham Childrens' Hospital, and Joan Richards, headmistress of the Firs Primary School, Castle Bromwich. With their help we decided to lend the cottage to recommended people who needed a quiet country holiday: there was neither telly nor telephone, but we had fun building up a little library of books we wanted to read ourselves but might not have indulged in otherwise. We charged for electricity and water, and there was a box labelled 'Small Subs. for the National Trust' (later, when things began to pinch, it was for 'Repairs and Replacements'.) We received a wealth of friendship and very few nasty shocks. Guests were asked to leave the place as they found it. Most left it better, cleaning and repairing so that our hearts warmed. To strangers we wrote 'No social obligations', even so we managed to see something of them all and reaped a rich harvest of experience. We heard hospital details from Birmingham and Great Ormond Street; school gossip from Lucton and Moor Park when parents stayed and their children came out to Hill Croft; and East End of London news from the many and various couples sent to us by Malcom Johnson, vicar of St. Botolph's, Aldgate.

We received invitations too, notably from the three Moor Park families, Dyckhoff, Sillars and Chisholm, who handed down Hill Croft from generation to generation of boys. Moor Park is a Roman Catholic prep. school near Ludlow. We have marvellous memories of summer Speech Days, with countless families and their dogs picnicking in groups on the playing fields. One of these dogs was the Chisholms' 'Abominable Laura', a darling yellow Labrador who ate part of the tapestry 'Welcome to Hill Croft' notice, the remains of which are treasured by Ruth Waugh. We remember too the winter shows, especially 'Toad of Toad Hall', given with great spirit in a

182

building where rain dripped through the roof and the weasels ran riot through the audience, uttering fearful cries!

Tom Adams was our first connection with Lucton schoolboys: we met him and a friend walking in the Lane one Sunday afternoon before our house building was finished and we enjoyed piloting the boys round the scaffolding cat-walk above our sitting room to be. Tom's parents, John and Peggy Adams, who farm in Warwickshire, came several times to Hill Croft while Tom and his brother Paul were at Lucton and we think of them often by the magnificent magnolia they gave us for our Hill Farm garden. With so many parents, boys past and present, staff and neighbours, they shared the dreadful shock of the school's abrupt closure at half term in the autumn of 1984. 'To avoid bankruptcy' was the reason given: the blow seemed personal to a whole community.

As the years went on we found that we could give less time to our Hill Croft guests. We were slower at our work, the hill is steep, and to accept warm offers to 'Come in' was fatal—we stayed far too long. Some could not understand this, and may have thought us unsocial and peculiar; but with some, five minutes talk on the doorstep and you felt you'd known them a life time. John Hunter was one of these—a tall, gentle old priest whose shining goodness is with us still. Bill Barton was another, also a priest, who touched the heart of things with a word. He and Gwen came twice—he did lovely sketches of round about—and Gwen came once, with a friend, Joan Harwood, after he died, because she said Hill Croft was full of Bill. We felt this too, it is a house of happiness, many have told us so. There were also anxious and odd times: once a young clerical gent made me tight on a warm summer evening—I failed to watch what he put in the brimming tumbler, managed to get out of the house all right (I think!) reeled on the forecourt, tottered up the Lane on Mary's arm and was violently sick for the rest of the evening. I've never touched gin and tonic since. Then there was a gremlin which always bothered the Bartons' visits: when they were here the pipes bumped, the water failed or the electricity went off at the crucial moment of tea making for a special guest, and poor Gwen had to tool up to us with her tea pot. At 6 o'clock one morning the milk delivery float tipped over with a terrible crash at their gate and shed most of its load down the Lane: Gwen, in her nightdress, insisted on helping us to sweep up broken glass, while Bill watched anxiously from the bedroom window—the last thing his poor heart needed.

The holiday at Hill Croft that disappointed most was probably the Burkles': David and Anne brought their young daughters Kate and Jo to what they thought was a 'working farm'—they had been before to places where the children had fed calves and handled lambs. I don't know who had recommended us to them—perhaps Great Ormond Street, because both girls had cystic fibrosis. When we discovered the enormity of this frightening family disease we were amazed at the courage it inspires: the relentless need for the parents to massage each child for twenty minutes twice daily, just to keep her alive; the struggle to have the children lead normal lives, however short; to get them off to school and David to his job—the mind boggles; and we couldn't even rustle up the jobs with animals for which they longed. Of course we invited them up to check the cattle and watch Jane fetch the sheep; but it dawned on us too late that they expected to be doing things themselves. Anyway it would have taken more organising that we could cope with—we were desperately tired at the time. To make matters worse David ricked his back in mid-holiday and couldn't help Anne with the massage. Our splendid local Health Service fixed him up with a collar at Leominster Cottage Hospital and would have helped with the girls' massage had they known the need in time; but the holiday was nearly over and the family returned to London. We felt we had let them down.

After this we decided to stop receiving 'recommendations' and confine our guests to those friends who knew the ropes; but the house was not properly occupied and often we felt guilty. Winters became increasingly difficult, when the Lane was impassable and we had to trudge down the field in deep snow to regulate the heating or thaw the frozen pipes. We thought how good it would be to have nearer neighbours, and discussed permanent tenants, a project we could consider now that the mains water was reliable; but to find the right people presented a problem indeed.

I had never met the Ashleys: they are both chiropodists, David practising in Hereford and Susan in Leominster, where for many years she had cared for Mary's feet. Mary always enjoyed her visits and came back to me with tales of good talk. I pictured Susan as rather a formidable lady in her fifties so I was surprised and delighted by the news of her pregnancy and by the radiant young woman with golden hair whom I met later on. Their third daughter Sarah was born in 1986, when Kate and Beth were already twelve and eleven years old.

We did not realise that the family wanted to live in the country until David rang to ask us about the holding just below Hill Croft, which had come up for sale: they were disappointed when it made more than they could afford. We wondered to ourselves about offering to let them the Hill Croft house, but we realised that we should have to build on to it for them and had not come to terms with that when Mary's illness struck.

She returned from hospital after eight anxious days and it was dark before I got out to do the evening jobs. I was in the road checking the forest gate locks when car headlights swept up: I was desperately tired and wanted no hold up, but it was a fair cop. A good-looking young man got out of the car with a 'Get Well' note for Mary and introduced himself as David Ashley: another two minutes and I would have been away up the bank with Jane, he would have dropped in the note and gone, and I would not have met him; as it was I knew beyond a shadow of doubt what I must do, and said 'We would let Hill Croft to you if you wished—go down the field and look round it and we'll talk again'. He disappeared into the dusk, I went on with Jane and returned to the house to tell Mary what I had done. We have never doubted, then or since, that it was the right thing.

We had thought vaguely about the letting: perhaps in a year or two... Now we realised that we must push on, and it was a blessing that we did, for we should never have coped with the building in the following year of Mary's next illness.

We roughed out a tentative plan for an extension and invited the Ashley family to an inspection and tea on Saturday the 11th of April 1987—a memorable date. We liked them all immensely and they loved Hill Croft, but Susan was troubled at the prospect of such a small house. We altered and enlarged the plans: here we were much helped by Hugh and Anne Dunsterville, who came as usual for a few days at Hill Croft (it was a sore wrench to say 'no more' to our friends.) Hugh worked out levels, because we were not sure whether the windows of the two planned rooms would come above the top of the bank made by the massive excavation needed. When we thought we had suggestions agreeable to the Ashleys and to ourselves we put them to Deacons, who soon produced a useful set of plans.

There followed a frustrating wait for the Council's permission, but as soon as it was given the JCB was upon us—disconcertingly so in fact, for it arrived on Saturday July 4th and worked on through the last weekend when my niece Emma and her family could be at Hill Croft, away from the noise of London.

Deacons had subcontracted the foundations to Mike Hogg, who soon gained our confidence with his quiet slow smile and perfectionist approach. His brother Chris worked the JCB, breaking down the bank with infinite care; but it hurt us to see the pulling apart of earth and rock and the gaping hole growing bigger and bigger until we realised that we had cut it too fine; we had to allow the removal of the gate posts and a small slice of the field to be included in the garden ground. The hundreds of tons of earth and stone removed were dumped in a long line on the disused cart track along the Cricket Pitch, beside, but not on top of, the snowdrop bank. The resulting heaps, stretching under the hedgerow along the length of the ground, looked ghastly; at the end they were levelled and are now green over, but we wondered what we were doing to the poor little place, and future generations will be puzzled by the alien plateau.

The weather was perfect high summer for the excavation week — had it rained the mess would have been awful. The foundation raft for the building was like a billiard table, smoothed down lovingly by Mike with a bonny little hand machine. It hurt him and us when many tons of breeze blocks were dumped on it because there was no room elsewhere on the steep site. Here the work picture changed: Mike's sub-contract continued and a large team of lads, plus the occasional girl friend, descended on us at weekends. They worked slap happy through rain and shine, the double walls rose quickly and the damp course went in all right — we were afraid that in the hectic haste it would be forgotten. They disconcerted us all by breaking a hole through the house wall without notice to Deacons, who had intended to do this tricky job with their own men: a large old beam stopped the boys half way, so that they had to dive under it to reach their work; but they were always pleasant and cheerful, though they made much mess. We were glad when Deacons' carpenters moved in.

After them came the roofers, again a gang of Mike's. We had imported thousands of old tiles which Deacons had stripped from Kington church. When we came to marry in the extension we found the existing house roof in such a poor condition that we must strip the lot; but apart from the expense, this was just as well because we were able to persuade the roofers (much cheered on by us from the side-lines) to do a marvellous tile mixing job so that the roof looks a pleasant mellow whole. The men ran up and down like monkeys, with much merry chat: at dinner time they disappeared down the valley and the afternoon was rent with song ('Abide with me' was a favourite tune) which did not help my writing up here. They flitted as fast as they worked: the last evening they left a tiny piece undone; next morning Mary greeted them at work, went round to the other side and spotted a smashed tile, returned to point it out and lo! they were gone! Mike made good the hole himself.

By mid-August the plasterers were in, the outside walls were rough cast, the whole outside was painted white. Beresford and Stephen fitted the new Rayburn cooker and completed the plumbing, Keith

Morgan finished the electricity job and the house was ready. The Ashleys took over on September 14th 1987.

Outside the picture was not so rosy: there was fencing to do, gate posts to set, the gate to be hung—we could not graze the field till this was done. We waited with growing impatience: finally Mike re-appeared with a long haired youth and an electric drill with which they then proceeded to bore enormous post holes: several holes were gaping when they came no more. We waited, daily expecting their return; but when David Ashley fell into one of the holes in the dark we rang Deacons. They sent a couple of men within two hours, and a good but rather lengthy finishing up job was completed. We haven't seen Mike since, but between us all, the result is a happy one, and the building is now much admired. David has done some beautiful carpentry work inside, and outside laid paving stones, recovered from the Cricket Pitch, to carry the car wheels. Susan's flowers, especially round the rocky walls of the 'Moat', are a summer joy.

The family have been with us for two years now: the comfort of their presence and the help at hand, so readily given, means much to us. That was a good night's work after hospital.

Hill Croft, 1989

XIV
Water

'Water is life' and I have spent much of mine trying to get the right amount in the right place.

At Armscote there was a well for each house, but through the farm only a stream which dried out in summer, when I trundled a two-wheeled water cart to the sheep. I learned the hard way that a suckling ewe will drink over a gallon a day in hot weather.

At Buckley Green there was no water in the fields. (How do people manage to farm stock without? Perhaps their wishful thinking founded the theory that sheep do not need to drink!) With the help of Mr. Lyne of Solihull and a government grant I sunk a bore hole whence unfailing water was pumped by electricity to every field.

At Brook Farm there was no easily accessible water; the sisters drove their cows across the road twice daily to drink their fill from the Pinsley Brook. I planned eight troughs between the flat little meadows, the water to be pumped up into a tank in the coach house loft. I thought we would need a bore hole, and as Mr. Lyne had done such a good job at Buckley Green I asked him to come from Warwickshire to do the Brook Farm scheme. We were pondering possible sites for a bore-hole when our neighbour, dear Mr. Tom Morgan, called over the hedge: 'You won't need to go deep for water—Kingsland wells never fail.' Neither did they until the year the River Lugg Drainage Board dredged the Pinsley Brook, lowering the water table so that all the wells in the vicinity went dry. The Board was obliged to deepen them all, at great cost—they had to go through rock for us at Brook Bridge, giving us a wonderful supply, though even this was unacceptable to the Milk Marketing Board later on.

Bringing water into Hill Croft was simple: when the Hereford Water Board brought the mains up the Lane in 1967 we took a branch to the house and Cricket Pitch, and put a single drinking trough between Top and Bottom. This was hard by the old pigscot, and when we replaced the cot with an 'agricultural building' (now described by the rating officer as a car port) we ran the rain water from the steep tiled roof into another drinking trough alongside the first: it is interesting that the cattle always prefer the rain water.

Bringing the water into Hill Farm was not so simple. The mains left the Lane at Hill Croft and came up our Lower Meadow: we plumbed it into the existing system (which supplied the house in a desultory way) so that we did not need then to break into the fabric; but this was a great mistake, for the existing system was not good. When I bought Hill Farm Mr. Hinton had just sunk a bore-hole in the orchard, built a half submerged reservoir in concrete, now mossy and mellowed, and erected a windmill to pump the water into the reservoir, whence it ran by gravity to two drinking troughs in the fields and to a tap in the yard. But the wind blew too little, the bore-hole often failed, and the reservoir emptied before the next breeze: we needed another reserve nearer the house. We put a large header tank in the granary, supplied by gravity from the orchard reservoir, and ran a pipe across the yard to the house; but this pipe was not laid deep enough and in every severe winter it froze—we never discovered where, but in several winters we were weeks without water for loos and bath. The tell-tale sound of drips into the house cistern was one of the thrills of the thaw. In theory we should have had a supply of drinking water in the kitchen tap because when we modernised the house we brought the rising main in on the south; but in practice, for about ten years, we had no mains water by day because the pressure was too poor to lift it further than Hill Croft. The more house building below, the worse was our supply: if we were late to

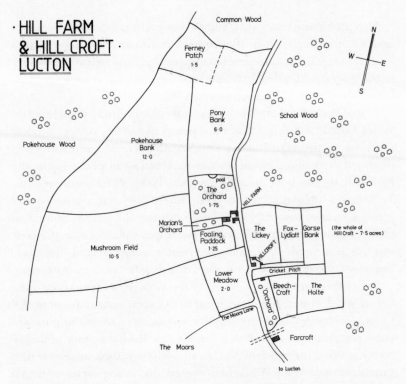

·HILL FARM
& HILL CROFT ·
LUCTON

Common Wood

Ferney
Patch
1·5

Pokehouse Wood

Pokehouse
Bank
12·0

Pokehouse
Bank
12·0

Pony
Bank
6·0

School Wood

HILL FARM

The
Orchard
1·75

pool

Marian's
Orchard

Foaling
Paddock
1·25

The
Lickey

Fox–
Lydiatt

Gorse
Bank

(the whole of
Hill Croft – 7·5 acres)

HILLCROFT

Mushroom Field
10·5

Lower
Meadow
2·0

Cricket Pitch

Beech–
Croft

The
Holte

Orchard

The Moors Lane

The Moors

Farcroft

to Lucton

bed we could fill buckets of drinking water for the following day; if
we missed that we must be early in the morning to catch the water
before it went; and if it did not come up at all during the night to
replenish our tanks we rang the Water Board depot in Leominster to
report a probable burst mains in the district. This was a frequent
happening: the Board was grateful for our information and offered
to reverse the calls charge; and they were always ready to send a
tanker to fill up the reservoir.

In the 1976 drought we were shattered to find that the cattle
could empty the house reserve tank in a day: we must separate their
supply from ours. Brains were brought to bear—this was our first
introduction to Beresford Vaughan, then working for Deacons but
now on his own with his splendidly qualified son Stephen.

191

The problem of the stock supply was eventually solved by a new underground reservoir in the Lower Meadow at mains level, with a submersible electric pump, servicing another tank below the header in the granary. The flow between the reservoirs was reversed and we hoped that our problems were over.

The Welsh Water Authority had taken over from the Hereford Water Board, and they installed a pump in Lucton village to boost water up to the high places. This greatly increased pressure overwhelmed the ball tap in our header tank and water poured from the high granary overflow, flooding the yard. Welsh Water countered this by fitting a regulator at the point where the mains entered our ground, but not before a joint blew in the ascending pipe, causing an underground leak for which we were responsible because the pipe was on our land. The spongy greener grass located the leak, Beresford dug down and it was soon mended; but worse was to come.

I was sitting in the Land Rover on the Grange in Leominster when I read Welsh Water's letter advising us of excess consumption at Hill Croft. The figures were unbelievable — thousands upon thousands of cubic metres in the last six months. We hurried home and found the meter reading normal and no sign of a leak — it took us several days to realise that Welsh Water had named the wrong meter and that Hill Farm was ticking madly away. We turned off the mains supply — the height of inconvenience — found no obvious leak and queried the functioning of the meter: Welsh Water tested to find it correct. They sent their men to look for a leak, with no success: it was never found. After three huge holes and a trench in the lawn (which has never been the same since) we established that the fault lay above the junction to the house, so we decided to re-route the rising main into the granary tanks, eliminating the pipe that ran under the house and concrete yard. The new route went through the hen run but the delicacy of the JCB digger was such that the hens were hardly disturbed; but while working in the Paddock it cracked a land drain through which was running a merry stream of water, presumably escaping from a burst beneath the new part of the house which had

192

been built over the pipe in 1970. The thought of water running away at that speed for over six months daunted us, as did the consumption bill from Welsh Water.

We contested the amount for years, claiming (a) that we had been misinformed and (b) that their excessive pressure had blown the joints. Our letters were ignored: the account came year after year until it wore us down and in the end we paid it. We now read both meters weekly.

The last straw came in 1986 when the granary supply to the house was frozen for three weeks. The night after the thaw came Mary and I went out in the dark to hang the bird table high in the prunus tree, ready for the morning. As we passed the barn we heard that awful grumbling sound from deep within the building—the old pipe to the granary had burst near the new joint despite the careful lagging. We found the stop cock, went to bed and rang Beresford in the morning. He and Stephen were with us within the hour, their brains combined and the dreaded decision was ours: we must abandon the granary and the Lower Meadow reservoir, (all that thought and work for nothing) replumb the house and depend entirely on Welsh Water for an uninterrupted supply—an act of faith indeed, after all the years. We siphoned hundreds of gallons from the granary tanks to run to waste on the yard, a sore experience for me; but the dreaded disruption in the house came to nothing: Beresford and Stephen completed the job in a morning, with little disturbance and no mess. With a new central heating boiler in the cloakroom instead of in the outside tack room the dread of frost and drought is over and we are cosy and happy with the water supply at last.

Happy, that is, provided that another Welsh Water bogey is really laid to rest. In 1984 they applied for and later received planning permission to construct a huge public service reservoir in Common Wood, on our northern boundary. We did not object formally, thinking far be it from us to hinder a needed supply and knowing that the application would be granted anyway, but the District Council did recommend that the very old oak trees on our boundary should be left undisturbed. Welsh Water agreed to this and so we took the opportunity to apply for a Tree Preservation Order for these and for over a hundred other trees on both farms; this was granted.

A representative from Welsh Water came to see us, bringing a plan which showed the ascending and descending mains cutting a wide swathe through the farm, dividing all three of our big fields from drinking water during the making, and ploughing through four hedgerows. The line went on across our neighbour's tillage, down over Mortimer's Cross Mill and under the bed of the River Lugg (an otter haven) to an unspecified supply in the valley. The prospect was awful.

With the Welsh Water man we paced out the probable site of the reservoir in Common Wood, working hard to have it as far from our boundary as possible—he wanted to share the fence, but this would disrupt the oak trees. Privately we marked a pipe line route through rails or gateways to avoid as much destruction to living growth as possible. We pictured the thousands of tons of concrete to be brought up Lucton Lane past our door, the noise of heavy machinery, the site buildings, the stone to be hauled off our farm where the pipe line had delved through the underlying rock. 'It would all be the same in the end' we were told: we knew that it would not.

We visited a similar scheme near Weobley, where the reservoir was nearly complete—a vast concrete structure, deep below and towering above ground. Part of an old oak wood had been felled and a beautiful little meadow was destroyed. Two hard approach roads had been made across the adjoining farm because one had proved inadequate. The finished pipe line scarred the field with a mass of weeds. The depressing prospect of a similar fate here haunted us for three years, until it was overshadowed by Mary's grave illness. We have heard no more from Welsh Water — dare we hope that the scheme is abandoned?

XV
Ferny Patch

When I received the deeds of Hill Farm in 1945 I noticed that a small patch of ground in the north-west corner was marked with a different colour from the rest of the fields. I asked the solicitor who was then acting for me, a local man, the reason for this and he replied that perhaps there were common rights—was the ground fenced into the farm from the adjoining woods? It was, with a stout wire fence. He suggested leaving it alone for a year or so, to see whether anyone made use of it, and if not I should feel free to go ahead with cultivations. I had no wish for any extra work but the war time duty to grow food was still heavy upon us and when Mary joined me in '47 we hired a contractor and set about clearing the scrub ready for ploughing.

We were cutting up silver birch for firewood one day when I looked up and saw a grim faced figure standing over me: it was one of the Lucton village elders, himself a farmer. 'What do you think you're doing here?' said he. 'Clearing the ground for ploughing' said I, full of virtue. 'You have no right at all to do this,' he went on—'it's common ground for stick gathering by the parish.' I answered that no-one had been near the ground during the two years of my ownership. 'We'll see about that' he said—'you'll be hearing from us' and he stumped off, leaving me aghast.

We were soon summoned to a meeting in the Lucton Parish Room at the Old Vicarage, a house opposite the school owned by the church but now let off, with the right of the Meeting Room reserved. The tenant, Mrs. Mawson, gave us a sympathetic welcome, but the whole affair seemed like a ghastly tribunal, with poker-faced people sitting around in judgement on a newcomer who would have done anything to put matters right. Finally it was settled that the Parish would receive the money for the sale of firewood (£30 to £40 as I remember it) with which we had hoped to pay the contractor, and that we should render to the Parish a 'rent' of £3 a year, the going rate per acre in those days. This money was held by a villager, with no proper accounts kept as far as I know, and when by common consent there was enough in the kitty, £1 each was handed out to householders, though Arthur, who paid this 'rent' when he became our tenant, never had a penny. This went on for over twenty years.

Under the Registration of Commons Act 1965 the Commons Commissioners set up a nationwide enquiry into the ownership of all common land. Our 'Ferny Patch' was inspected on behalf of Herefordshire County Council by Mr. O.K. Ford, who was kind enough to come down to see us at Brook Farm—this was in the late 1960's. He had found that Ferny Patch was not even within Lucton Parish boundary but in the adjoining one of Aymestrey. He thought that we had a very strong case for registering ownership and advised us to apply. We did, and thought no more for several years, but found that at the last minute before the register closed the Lucton parishioners had persuaded the headmaster, Mr. Keith Vivian, to sign an objection, although he knew little of the affair. This meant that the case must come up for a public hearing, no doubt in the far future—we tried to put it out of our minds; but of course when we took over from Arthur in 1970 we did not resume 'rent' paying because the matter was subjudice, as we tried to explain to various neighbours who approached us with little hints and digs which at first we did not even understand. Finally we invited the headmaster to come up and look for himself at the ground, which was now in grass and graced by the seventeen beautiful oak trees which we had left when we cleared the coppice. Mr. Vivian seemed never before to have looked at Ferny Patch, but even when we pointed out that there was no public right of way into it from any direction he remained unconvinced that it must belong to Hill Farm.

At last, in February 1981, we were called to a hearing before the Commons Commissioner, Mr. A. Baden Fuller, at the Shire Hall, Hereford. We had decided not to have a solicitor to represent us, but I prepared a statement which we submitted to the Commissioner beforehand, and we also took the farm deeds and several other old documents which might be relevant to our case.

We went early to the Shire Hall and with butterflies in our tummies climbed the steep steps to red plush seats in the tiered court room. The Commissioner sat remote at the high desk, his clerk beside him; there was a sprinkling of people around the court, but no-one we knew except Mr. Ford, who had come to support us—we were so grateful to him. We had expected the headmaster and some of the other Lucton objectors, but not a soul had bothered to turn up.

When our case was announced I was not called to speak: the Commissioner had my statement in front of him, and asked for objectors—there were none. He then dismissed us and sent a clerk to telephone the headmaster in Lucton to ask if he would withdraw the objection. The reply came back in no time: 'Yes, certainly', and we were recalled to hear the verdict: we are the registered owners of 'Ferny Patch' and there is no common claim. So ended a long-lasting storm in a tea-cup which cost us dear in time and trauma.

When our registration papers came through we wrote to the Lucton Parish Committee explaining what had happened and sent a final donation of £30 in lieu of lapsed 'rent'. We received in reply a charming letter of thanks: that money, plus presumably some accumulation over the years, was the basis of the fund, now administered by the Lucton Residents' Association, and used for the good of the village and for donations to various charities.

Ferny Patch is a beautiful place, a rich reward for climbing Pony Bank. The level plateau of good grass falls sleepily down to meet Pokehouse Wood in a slope covered in season with anemones, blue-bells, violets, lady's slipper, wood sorrel—a wealth of wild flowers.

Many of the big oaks stand here, though one was felled during Arthur's tenancy, which hurt us greatly. Recently we asked Hereford and Worcester County Council for a Tree Preservation Order: Their officer Mrs. Graves gave much of her time to a comprehensive survey of both farms. Over the years we have planted along the hedgerows many young oaks, grown by us from acorns or baby saplings in pots and then brought on in a little nursery at Hill Croft. Guarding the hedgerow trees against stock is costly in time and energy and we have several more to plant. Many of the trees are named for friends, dead or alive: there is a space waiting for Pamela's oak next to Raymond's, the last planted and doing well. Mrs. Graves included in the order all the young and mature trees, a total of a hundred and eighteen. We are grateful for her care and the protection of the County Council.

Ferny Patch is a favourite jumping out place for the deer who come in regularly to feed. We welcome them on the meadows but not in the garden which they have just discovered. They are full fed when they push in here, so wander plucking such titbits as rose buds, lupin heads and lettuce.

The deer in Mortimer Forest are culled by the Forestry Commission's deer wardens, good country men and good rifle shots. This is a humane way of death, quietly grazing and then—nothing. But here there are sometimes horrible hang-ups. The boundary fences to the wood are pig wire with a top strand of barbed and a careless or hurried jump can leave a hind leg caught, so that the animal hangs on the fence head down until he is found or dies. When we find one a phone call to the warden brings him in half an hour and a point blank shot finishes the pain; but we cannot patrol all the boundaries daily. Once we found a buck on Hill Croft hanging dead after days of agony. The ideal would be a wooden top rail throughout, but the work is too great. We look the best we can and try never to hurry deer off the fields. Ferny Patch is far and quiet and a very special place for us all.

XVI
Welsh Mountain Ponies

For years during our sheep showing career we had admired the Welsh Pony parades at the Royal Welsh: we remember the stallion Tregoyd Starlight being run out in the triumph of his championships, and the warm and dignified presence of Miss Daisy Brodrick showing her famous Coed Coch ponies. We wrote to her asking if we might come to her for mares when our sheep days were over: we treasure her reply but were sad that she died before we started. We had no idea of founding a stud and knew little of what we wanted—just a couple of small mares to breed from and keep us happy in our 'retirement'.

One afternoon in 1969 Jean Houghton walked down the sheep line at the Three Counties Show with a possible purchase in mind. We fell into talk and found that she owned the Sinton Stud of Welsh ponies at Hallow, near Worcester. She was interested in our plans for the future and invited us to visit her: we sold each other neither sheep nor ponies but Jean helped us to know without doubt that Welsh Mountain ponies (Section A in the Stud Book) were what we wanted. Sinton Brownie was for sale, a beautiful bay pony who went on to breed winners in the south. We longed to have her, but she was Section B and would need more care and cover than we felt prepared to give. Section B Welsh ponies are bigger—up to 13.2 hands high—and more finely bred than Section A, the Welsh Mountain, who are the foundation of the Welsh breed: they must be under 12 hands, but 'strong enough to carry a man all day on the mountain', hardy to live out in all weathers, lively and proud of presence. They were the ponies of our dreams. Jean helped us to realise this: that visit to her was memorable and happy—she was the first of several very close friends brought to us by our ponies.

Maybe it would have been sensible to look on the mountains for those first mares, to keep to the old adage: 'always buy stock from west to east'; but we needed then no extra travel, and at the Royal we found Pip and her daughters Patience and Prue. Dorothy and Alun Mathias who farmed at Granby, near Armscote, had brought the pony family to the show and both the fillies were in the prize money. In the autumn we went to see them at home and our first sight was of the grey mare Pip (Granby Pepita, by Clan Pip) looking magnificent as she gazed over the fence after her newly weaned foal—clever showmanship by Dorothy, who told us afterwards that 'Pip was not really a show mare'. We walked on across the farm to see the fillies and found a large bunch of young ponies on the rough side of Brailes Hill, with the rolling Warwickshire countryside stretching away below. It was 'mountainy' enough for us and anyway we had fallen for Patience and Prue, who were charming and easy to handle, like all the Granby ponies. We tried hard to buy all three as a family, but Dorothy wanted to keep one of the fillies, so we settled for Pip and her two year old daughter Patience. We bespoke them and it was arranged that they should come to us in foal after our sale the following year.

To our surprise and delight Dorothy and Alun turned up at the Brook Farm sale and bought some sheep and many lots of tools and oddments: they boosted the trade immensely and we thought it very good of them to come so far to help us. The following week they delivered Pip and Patience and our pony breeding began.

In the spring of 1971 both mares brought colt foals with no fuss or trouble at all: we had yet to learn how seldom native ponies need help and had even advised our vet of probable foaling dates. We handled the colts from birth and sold them privately, at weaning time, to be brought on as children's ponies: the demand for these was still good and we planned to clear all foals before the winter work set in.

Pip and Patience had now to be served again and we consulted Dorothy Mathias about what stallion to use. To our surprise she offered to lend us 'a little Revel stallion' provided that he could bring a mare along with him to run with ours for the summer. The Revel, with Emrys and Dinah Griffiths, was one of the top studs in the breed: we thought it too good a chance to miss.

We drove to Warwickshire to fetch him in some anxiety, never before having handled a stallion; but he had been at Granby since a foal and Dorothy assured us that he was easy. How easy we did not realise fully until we compared him with others later.

We found a stout little chestnut pony, very small, very rough, with tremendous bone, a keen sharp head and tiny ears half hidden by shaggy mane. His name was Revel Savoury and he was a grandson of the great Coed Coch Madog. Dorothy called him the Rabbit because when Emrys showed him to her she had exclaimed: 'What, that little rabbit!' We called him Rab and kept quiet about his size.

Of course he needed more mares and anyway we were bitten by the breeding bug, so we went again to Granby to find a couple of nice fillies. We were shown a lovely golden dun two year old by Coed Coch Aelwyn: while we were looking at her there came around us a tiny roan creature, trotting full tilt, with mane and tail streaming, head high, ears pricked, a picture of a mountain pony. She moved like a dream and we asked about her sire. 'She's no use to you' replied Dorothy, 'she's by the Rabbit.' We turned away, but the little pony came again and ran rings round us: we couldn't keep our eyes off her and in a fit of lunacy we bought her: ('After all it would be interesting, taking her to other studs'!) We bought the dun as well, and came home with Granby Thaisa and Granby Cassandra: we called them Mustard and Cress.

In 1971 we took Cress to Lord Kenyon's Gredington stud in Shropshire, where we were impressed by the individual handling of visiting mares: she returned in foal to the famous old Coed Coch

Planed but brought us a colt. In 1972 we tried for a foal from Coed Coch Norman, who was standing at Mrs. Hambleton's Llanerch stud in Montgomeryshire before his export to Australia. Cress ran with him there for six weeks and returned, presumed in foal, to be turned out by us, in our inexperience, with the other mares and Rab on the bank. Three weeks later, on my Sunday evening round, I was horrified to find her, obviously 'on', being hotly pursued by her father. I went straight back to the house for Mary and two halters and from an alarming melée we extracted Cress, shut her in a box for the night and rang Mrs. Hambleton: could we bring Cress back to Norman next day? But Norman had gone already, it was so late that all the stallions were away from the mares, it would be inconvenient but we could try her with Sinton Solomon if we wished—there would be no charge. With hindsight of course we should have left things as they were, but back up to the Llanerch we went and Cress was turned out with Solomon. A few days later came a telephone call: please would we come and remove Cress at once, she was certainly not on, they could do nothing with her, we had spoilt the pony. (This hurt, as with us she handled sweetly.) We toiled off to Montgomeryshire again next day, caught her easily and brought her home to run with the good nanny Pud at Hill Croft.

By this time I was thoroughly tired of all the driving and the hassle and we decided to sell Cress, barren as we thought her, to make a child's riding pony. Jean Houghton found her a good home with the grandchildren of Mr. Prosser of the Byfields Stud of Welsh Cobs (Section D). They were delighted with her, and even more so when their mother rang us late the following summer to tell that without warning Cress had brought them a lovely foal! We were pleased to be able to hand to Mrs. Hambleton Solomon's stud fee, which may have compensated a little for the trouble we gave; but since I started to write this chapter it has come to me: of course that foal was by Rab!

We had expected that Rab would return to Granby at the end of the season, but Dorothy asked if we would keep him for the winter. We agreed, provided that it was all right to run him on with the mares—we could not cope with a stallion separate, to be housed and exercised. He stayed with them sweetly and in all the years we had him we never moved him from his mares.

Come the spring Dorothy wondered whether we would care to buy Rab. We demurred, still without confidence in ourselves as stud owners—it was not at all the role we had planned. We were still undecided when we delivered our caravan to Dorothy and Alun, who had bought it because Alun was tired of sleeping in the straw at shows. We were invited to lunch and when Dorothy went out of the room to prepare we were left alone with the youngest daughter, Veronica, then about six years old. No sooner had the door closed than she turned upon us with gleaming eyes and said: 'How much are you going to give us for the Rabbit?' We were vastly amused, decided to go ahead and when Dorothy returned we were able to negotiate a reasonable price and Rab was ours.

The news soon got around that a Section A stallion was running out at Lucton and we were besieged with enquiries from people wanting to bring mares or fillies: the telephone rang incessantly and Mary seemed forever engaged in long listening to the problems of peculiar ponies—the talks were endless and nearly drove me crazy. We took all and sundry—fillies, barren mares, the lot—and turned them out with the bunch. The constant crack of hooves on Rab's chest echoed from the bank and we were always anxious; but our customers were pleased, for he got their mares in foal.

One gentleman from not far off brought a little brown mare and her good foal to run with Rab: they were here only a few days, though we preferred to keep mares over three weeks to make sure they held to the first service. We were a bit puzzled by the dates when he rang a few weeks later and said that his mare had turned—could he bring her back and please may she be served in hand? We assured him that this was not our job at all, but he was very pressing and we agreed to have a go. We fetched Rab in, the mare was unloaded and we all went into the orchard where Rab, in Mary's hands, performed quietly and well. When we remarked on the foal's absence the gentleman replied that he thought it better to shut him up at home rather than have a hassle here, which seemed fair enough; but we were surprised when the mare was very reluctant to re-load—last time she had gone easily into the trailer. While we were helping to urge her up the ramp we each noticed a snip of white on her forehead which was not there before. They drove away down the hill without delay, leaving us incredulous as we realised that it was a different mare. Two services for one stud fee and so sharply done! We regarded it as a small price to pay for the experience.

In Rab's second season Pip and Patience kept returning to him and we were really worried. Our vet traced the trouble to a diseased visiting mare who was removed at once, ours were washed out and were soon in foal again, late as it was. Rab never left us a barren mare.

That was the end of visitors: we decided to settle down with a small stud of our own, but we needed another mare or two so we went to the top of the tree.

Jean Houghton took us to The Revel that first time: it was a mountainy day, with rain in the wind. We drove through Talgarth up into the Black Mountains, stopped in the shadow of Mynydd Troed and looked across at the Trimmer and the Cradle; then down the hill, up the lanes and into the yard, with Dinah's new garden in flower, the sound of running water in our ears and a glimpse of mares and foals in the paddocks below. No sign of Emrys but Dinah welcomed us into the parlour where we sat talking too long for our ache to get to grips with the job of the day. (Our sheep buying experience had taught us that this beginning is customary and polite but we ached none the less.) At last Emrys came and we were soon among them, seven or eight of the best mares at The Revel, we darting here and there, Emrys leaving us ('Have a good look on your own now') and we after him ('What's this by? How's that one bred?') Then three or four drawn out and running up and down the lane, Emrys turning them ('Take your time now') and we not able to take our eyes off Toots, with her grand dun colt streaming beside her. Then Toots and

Julie drawn to the rick yard, brief conferences, round again, a hunt for Emrys, always the other end ('Are you sure now? Julie would be more homely') and then the final swift hand touch and his glorious smile and she was ours.

It came to us afterwards that Emrys never meant to sell Toots: she was brought down with the others on account of her colt, for whom Emrys also had customers that afternoon. They were Brian and Betty French, of the Forlan Stud, now our close friends but then we did not meet. Emrys kept us apart with skill and only came to the house for us when the deal for Revel Torc was concluded, and Brian and Betty had driven away. There was memorable business done that day at The Revel: Torc at eighteen is still with the Frenchs, one of the best known and most successful stallions in the breed.

Toots had been sent away before we bought her and was believed in foal to Nutbeam Crispie, an out-cross which Emrys wanted for one of his best mares; but it was just not her thing to run in and out of lorries—she was a wild mountain pony and we believe that she had never been haltered before Emrys began to handle her for us. She must have fought him every inch of the way, resenting the prisoning stable, struggling against the restraining halter, refusing to eat, perhaps absorbing the foal inside her. When we went to fetch her we found a sad creature tied in the stable: she was thin and miserable and an anxious Emrys kept saying: 'If you don't like her you bring her straight back'.

We were puzzled by this until we got her home and then we knew what he meant. We ran her into our trailer, out again into a big double loose box, the old cow pen, and left her with hay and water for the night.

Next morning we could not get near her. When we approached she tried to climb up the far wall; failing that she turned her back and lashed out: she was not nasty but frightened for her freedom. For days we went in and out of her box frequently and sat on the manger talking to her: she ate her feeds when we had gone and the tension eased a little, but still she forbade our approach. I spent sleepless nights of worry and at last decided with myself that we must return her to The Revel. It was in the days when Mary was able to give me Sunday mornings off work and I lay in bed, unable to read, screwing myself to tell her of my decision. She was later than usual coming round under my window and before I could say a word she exclaimed 'I've done it! I've got a head collar on her!' I was appalled at the risk Mary had taken on her own and told her that Toots must go; but Mary was adamant: on no account would we part with her. I had to give way.

We left the head collar on day and night for a while, a dangerous practice with ponies, as they can get caught up and strangle themselves. In time we were able to clip on a cord and lead her out across the yard to Marian's Little Orchard, where she spent the day by herself. At night she ran into her box along a hurdle fence we contrived to guide her off the lawn: only once were we ever able to catch her in the field.

Come spring it was obvious that Toots was not in foal. Emrys was concerned and promised to give us a filly in the autumn; meanwhile he offered to get her in foal again at The Revel. We accepted gladly, being anxious about turning her away on a big run with Rab. She returned in foal to Revel Janus and brought a colt the following year. Thereafter she ran happily with Rab.

When we went to fetch the promised filly foal we found waiting for us a dark, shaggy little creature with four stout legs and a big coat. The first of our friends who saw her asked 'Did her mum meet a Shetland on the mountain?' We called her Revel Trim: she made a fine grey mare with the eye of an eagle.

We thought we needed still one more mare to do Rab justice and when Lady Rosamund Greaves (now the Countess of Dysart) brought many of her ponies to the Fayre Oaks sale at Hereford we were able to buy old Coed Coch Cysclys, mother of Cilcain, so at last we had a pony handled by Miss Brodrick herself and our stud was full.

We had a hair-raising journey home from Hereford with Cysclys: we made the mistake of tying her in the trailer and before we were out of the sale yard she was throwing herself madly about, to the cries of knowledgeable bystanders: 'Loose her off, loose her off!' We did so, but before we were a hundred yards into the traffic she began rearing up in a desperate effort to escape. We stopped again, and Mary got into the trailer with her, haltered her and travelled home stroking and talking. The old thing soon became quiet and we were never troubled by her again; but I drove on in great anxiety, knowing nothing of what went on in the trailer behind me. Mary was very tired by the time we got home.

With six good mares established we changed our selling plans: we tried still to clear the colt foals to private buyers but wintered the fillies and regularly entered them the following autumn at Fayre Oaks, thereby ensuring a good place in the sale order and a hoped-for reputation for reasonable price reserves. Fayre Oaks at Hereford is the Breed Society's premier sale for both Sections A and B, and is probably the largest and certainly the most important sale of these Welsh ponies in the world. It is so-named because it began in 1954 as a reduction sale for a leading breeder, Theron Wilding-Davies (father of Paul) on his Fayre Oaks Farm near Hereford. To enlarge the trade other breeders sent selected ponies until the number outgrew the place and in 1958 the sale was moved to Russell, Baldwin and Bright's yard in Hereford market. Here it flourished, still an 'invitation sale', until 1970 when the Welsh Pony and Cob Society adopted it, under the same auctioneers, as an official breed society sale. Buyers come from all over the world in September each year and expect to find top quality: it is very hard to sell indifferent ponies at Fayre Oaks.

Rab was getting some lovely bay and chestnut foals. Grey predominates in the Welsh Mountain breed but 'colour' had become very fashionable and our ponies were admired. We took Mustard's bay filly Marmite to Fayre Oaks in 1974 and there was much interest in her, notably from a tall lady of grace and presence, who asked to see the pony's paces. I led Marmite through the crowded sale yard, weaving in and out of people and ponies to reach the running-out alley, where she gave a sweet show and returned calmly to our pen. We all marvelled that a youngster who had never before been outside the farm gate should behave so well: she became a perfect children's pony.

Anne Dunsterville bought Marmite and there began one of the closest friendships in our life together. She took the wind out of our sails that day by asking us to take Marmite home for the night and bring her again to Hereford next morning to load on a Wiltshire bound lorry. We were always exhausted after sale days and heaved a sigh of relief when our responsibility ended with the fall of the hammer. Of course we did it, but I could not face the return journey next day. Mary took Marmite back alone, loaded her successfully with other ponies and also kept a dentist appointment at Hereford hospital in the afternoon—a fraught day and I have always regretted my defection and the lost chance of another meeting with Anne.

She herself is a breeder of Connemara ponies: her purchase of Marmite—known afterwards as Minnie—was with an eye for grand-children, but this did not work out: Marmite still belongs to Anne but is now much loved by a family of children in Kent—there is a photograph of her grazing placidly at a show.

We caught the showing bug early in our pony career. In 1971 the Kingsland Show was held at Croft, in a beautiful setting below the terrace of the Castle. The Mather family were at Hill Croft for the weekend and they helped us, looking after Pip and her foal while we returned home to fetch Mustard and Cress. It was all huge fun: we enjoyed being together in the ring once more and everyone was very welcoming to our first show with ponies. It was first time too for the judge, Paul Wilding-Davies, who put Pip second in the mare class and the yearling filly Mustard overall champion Welsh pony: we were tickled to bits!

The following year we flew higher and entered Patience and her foal at the Three Counties, the Royal and the Royal Welsh. She was cream, with flaxen mane and tail and she washed up beautifully at home, but it was anxious work removing travelling and stable stains

With mares and foals near Ferny Patch, 1972

at the show. We felt the novices we were but learnt a great deal: at the Three Counties the judge, Mrs. Egerton, gave me a valuable tip in presentation; at the Royal, as we were parading, I heard Dorothy Mathias remark from a ringside seat: 'Too much mane, Miss Wenham'. We took it all in and tried to mend our ways.

At the big shows that first year we hired a stable and slept the night before judging in the trailer on the show ground: the distance to the Royal was too great for us to drive in the early morning. Afterwards we limited ourselves to the Three Counties and the Royal Welsh and did it in the day, but we wanted to go to one Royal with a pony, among other things to gratify Anne Leigh's expressed wish 'to watch us running in our plimsolls'! She was wheeled to our ringside and we saw her radiant smile for the last time.

Maybe we had not given enough thought to the job of running out a show pony: one needs to run well and straight beside the pony at an extended trot. A sheep acquaintance remarked ungallantly that we had shown our animals the wrong way round in our lives. I thought he was wrong as he said it because I had found trimming

209

show sheep so hard on the eyes towards the end; but I am thirteen years older than Mary and she did most of the running.

The distances within the show ground were another snag to our pony showing at the Royal: between stables and collecting ring seemed miles and the way was not roped off in those days, so that mare and foal and leaders must thread through the crowds in the road ways. We were anxious about not arriving on time for our class and said as much to Big John from Coed Coch, whose ponies were stabled near us. 'I'll let you know when I'm going out' he said—'then follow me'. We did so and arrived in the ring in good order: we were very grateful for that kindness.

We did moderately well showing Patience, never in the money but always in the middle of the large classes, which was all we dared hope. Afterwards we gave up showing a mare and foal and took one of the yearling fillies, who looked well after the good wintering we gave them. They were stabled by night, with three small feeds and hay ad lib, led out each morning to Marian's Orchard, and fetched back after muck-out for handling and grooming. We did not rug up the show ponies to hasten their coats off but Mary managed it by hard strapping with dandy and body brush, rubber grooming glove and strong massage with the flat of the hand. It was grinding hard work but the ponies shone. We washed them all over with soap and lots of tepid water the day before the show and took turns to school them running out. The days were not long enough, for the gardening and stock rounds had to be done as well—the mares and foals and the Cwmwhitton sheep and cattle—and we were getting very very tired.

At 4.15 a.m. on May 11th 1974 Toots brought her first foal by Rab. Mary was in the offing near the Paddock but came back to bed when she saw that the foal was all right. When we looked in daylight we could see that the foal was a chocolate coloured filly, soon to turn grey; as she followed her mother we exclaimed 'Too good to be true!' She was named Lucton Toogood.

We were soon able to handle her with no objection from Toots. We all went quietly through the summer, hardly believing that we had bred such a beauty and not wanting to raise false hopes; but Nell Pennell, famous founder of the Bwlch Stud, saw her when she was still a baby and left us saying 'I shall dream of that tonight'.

Toogood wintered well and grew a lot. We took her to the Three Counties with open minds: perhaps she might be placed in the large class? She was pulled in first without question—first prize yearling filly at a major show! We could hardly believe it.

The Royal Welsh was a different matter: Without doubt it is the premier show in the world for Welsh ponies—the quality there is absolute tops—a first prize at the Royal Welsh is an incomparable accolade. We hoped that Toogood might be in the front line.

She swung into the ring with her usual striding walk and Mary looked proud of her. From the ringside I counted over thirty yearling fillies. The judge was one who knew his own mind and they had hardly completed a circle when Toogood was called in to stand first—a call so unexpected that Mary missed it and was urged in from the ringside. I could hardly believe my eyes; but there was a long way to go yet. Each pony is called out to give an individual show before the judge: a long hard wait for me, but still Toogood stayed at the top. At last they were all sent round again and recalled to the final placing: Toogood was first prize yearling filly at the Royal Welsh! As she and Mary ran in from their lap of honour I ran beside them gasping 'Good old things!' A delighted laugh from the ringside sealed our joy: together we had done it!

Toots brought a colt the following year but in 1976 she and Trim each had a bay filly, Tookind and Triad. We showed them both as yearlings which was silly because of the work, but we were so proud of them. The Three Counties was a disaster for us: it was a pouring wet day, the grass in our ring was ankle deep, the essential wellies hampered running and I could not hold Triad to a steady walk; we were a nuisance to ourselves and to other exhibitors. When the judge had placed her eighth he came to me and said: 'You did not do your pony justice'. It was a bitter pill. She was third at the Royal Welsh in a much bigger class, but Mary ran her out.

We had great faith in Triad and showed her again as a two year old, a difficult job as the classes are for twos and threes and the younger ponies tend to be outfaced. She was first at the Three Counties and won the reserve championship after a close struggle for the top honour. At the Royal Welsh she was not placed but the 'ringside judges' thought well of her.

We looked now to the future. We wanted to keep Toogood and Triad, which meant that we must part with Rab. All the work had become too much for us and we decided to reduce quietly down again to two mares, but this time to two tops of our own breeding. We set about finding good homes.

Rab went to Joy Brookes of the West Bradeney Stud; Toots and Cyclys to Brian and Betty French; Pip, Patience and Mustard to smaller breeders; while Trim joined Rab later at West Bradeney.

To save ourselves travel we planned to take Toogood and Triad to the best stallion we could find within reasonable distance; but when we mentioned this to Emrys he replied: 'I wouldn't bother to take a mare down the road, (he did, but still!) I'll lend you something.' We thought this a grand idea and thanked him warmly.

When the time came we went to The Revel to collect Rhiwia Titw (pronounced Titou), a mature premium stallion due soon to run with many mares on the mountain. 'You can have him for a fort-night' said Emrys. We gasped: we should be fortunate to get two mares in foal in a fortnight. As luck would have it Toogood was right on when we turned him out: there was a beautiful service and we felt sure she would hold. She loved him and they spent the next few days snugly together, while Trim and her foal wandered on their own.

Well under the fortnight the telephone rang: it was Emrys— 'Please bring Titw back tomorrow.' We pleaded for a few more days but Emrys was adamant: 'But don't worry—I've a colt for you to cover with.' We had no choice. We did not even know whether we could catch Titw; he had not been out of the field since he came and he would not want to leave Toogood. We were on our own—there was no-one there to help run him in. My heart was in my mouth as I

212

approached him with feed bucket and halter. He was lying down with Toogood and did not bother to get up as I slipped on the halter. Then he came as good as gold. He was a splendid little horse and Toogood brought a lovely grey filly foal by him: we called her Lucton Twt, which means in Welsh 'neat' or 'tidy': she is now with Mrs. Binnie of the Brockwell Stud.

We drove off again on the now weary way to The Revel. Emrys was waiting for us, and took us straight to the barn where we were horrified to find a dirty grey bag of bones, the two year old colt Revel Polish. Emrys was apologetic: the pony had been running with a lot of young colts in East Anglia: 'He'll soon come on your good ground'.

I backed the trailer up to the barn door and we ran him in: on return home we ran him out again into the big bull box, fed him and left him for the night. He was sweet and quiet and our spirits rose.

Next morning we haltered him which he accepted readily. We tried to lead him out, but he would not stir, and no persuasion moved him: he did not understand what we wanted—obviously he had been haltered but never led. We did not want a trial of strength and anyway time was important, so we backed the trailer up again, ran him in and drove him the hundred yards to Pony Bank, where we loosed him out to an indifferent Toogood and a curious Trim, whom he served in due course. There we left him and here we made a crashing mistake. We were used to Rab, who stayed all the year round with his mares and we did not realise the damage that could be done by leaving a stallion out. Soon after the turn of the year Polish began pestering Toogood, not much at first but she hated it. When they began galloping we knew that we must act: we got him in and there we were, landed with the work that we had always resisted—a stabled stallion, and an unhandled one at that.

He was soon persuaded to lead, first on the yard, then around the fields. Mary was superb: for months she strapped him daily, led him increasing distances up the banks and schooled him to run out straight. He muscled up and became a handsome well-mannered pony. Mary muscled up too, but it was an awful strain.

Toogood foaled safely and when we thought she was ready we turned Polish to her: she would have none of him. We tried again each day but it was no good. The next heat we held her and presented him in hand: she struggled and I could not hold her. With an experienced helper it was the same: Toogood hated Polish and there it was. In the end we gave it up and took Polish back to The Revel. We were disappointed that Emrys was haymaking so did not see the tidy pony who emerged from our trailer. Polish is now a show stallion with Mr. and Mrs. Harry Parsons of The Quinton Stud near Birmingham.

Toogood remained barren that year. It was late in the season when we finished trying with Polish and although the Frenchs, who supported us through thick and thin, would have brought her to and from Wiltshire to one of their stallions, we decided to let it go and start again in good time the following year.

In 1979 we settled down to our original plan and for three years running we took Toogood and Triad to Rosemary Philipson-Stow's Pendock Stud near Tewkesbury. It was an easy drive for us and there were always good stallions: but in 1981 Toogood proved barren again.

We were deeply despondent. I was tired of the driving and of the hassle and longed to say to Mary 'let's give it up now'; but I couldn't. The ponies meant so much to her: it never occurred to me that she would bear to part with them. When Brian and Betty came to fetch Toogood for Forlan Blue Boy I expected to see her back in nine weeks time; but Mary had decided that she would never come back. She wept when she told me: I was touched and devastated, but relieved beyond words.

We collected Triad from Pendock in foal to Criban Brenin. Brian and Betty came in the autumn to fetch her and our two mares were together again in one of the top studs in the breed. They have been there eight years now and their progeny are well known at shows all over the country: Toogood herself, with a grand foal beside her, was champion at Abergavenny in 1985. Best of all for us we have been able to visit them each year, thanks to the great kindness of our Wiltshire friends.

After the purchase of Minnie Marmite Hugh and Anne Dunsterville came each year for a few days at Hill Croft, bringing with them their two or three little bitches—dachshunds and a pug. In time we were persuaded to visit them at Halse and there began the annual autumn weekends which have meant so much in our life. Raymond and Pamela held the fort at Hill Farm and we spent two days and nights in another world.

At first we drove down the M4 and over the Severn Bridge—good experience, but we hated the motorway in the Landrover; then we tried the Gloucester by-pass, but I scraped the side of a car on a roundabout in Stroud so we avoided that town in future and settled for the lovely cross-country way through Frocester and Westonbirt. When we skirted the chalk downs near Westbury and viewed the White Horse above us we were getting on; after Warminster, through the lanes by the River Wylye, we were nearly there; and as we drove down the village street of Sutton Veny and turned, opposite the church, into the Halse drive our hearts rose to meet the marvellous welcome there. We were home and dry.

Halse House has the grace of a country mansion and the feel of a family home. The high hall rises to a small gallery whence bedrooms lead southwards to overlook lawn and garden and the paddocks beyond. We dined in the carpeted kitchen from a polished table set with silver, while the little bitches lounged against the Aga on the other side of the room. Food and wine were fabulous and we were

215

well content. Afterwards we sat in the small sitting room, presided over by Fanny the Dove who lived there in a huge cage which had been her home ever since she was rescued from death as a squab: her gentle voice murmured at intervals through the house. We talked and laughed long into the night: once, when I doubted the existence of God, Anne expressed surprise that one of my intelligence could feel such doubt. Her intelligence equals mine: I have pondered that remark.

Afterwards we went up to bed in our cosy little suite and woke to the skyline sweep of the downs across our window and the sound of rooks setting off for the day: I never hear one now without thinking of Halse.

Cups of tea were brought to us and later Anne and Hugh came with breakfast trays—coffee, cornflakes, boiled eggs, toast and marmalade—such luxury, such kindness we could hardly believe as we ate at leisure, side by side in the comfy beds.

During the days they showed us bits of Wiltshire—the downs, the villages and twice we went to the Wylye Horse Trials. Longleat was an experience, but spoilt for me by the anger of the gorilla, solitary on an island, who beat his chest and shouted at us hugely; none of us liked that. Best of all was the Sunday morning prowl round Anne's lovely ponies: Mylerstown Peach and Fuchsia, the Connemara mares; Mylerstown Sevilla, the winning riding pony; and Sevilla's chestnut children, all descended from old Catherston Fairy Dewdrop, Anne's famous foundation mare.

When our own ponies came to Wiltshire we longed to see them from time to time. Brian and Betty gave us the warmest of invitations to Toplands Farm: tentatively we asked Hugh and Anne if we might go to Slaughterford on the Saturday of our weekends with them: it seemed to us like treating Halse as an hotel and we felt badly about it; but we were met with total understanding. I hated driving out again so soon, back through the Chippenham traffic, but the Frenchs' glowing welcome put us right on top of ourselves again.

Brian and Betty, with their son Jeremy, work harder than any small farmers we have known. Long before the present diversification craze they were exploring every avenue to make a go of supporting a family on a small acreage. They have pedigree ponies, pedigree cats, Welsh Mountain sheep (older ewes brought down from The Revel) and poultry galore, mostly free range—no battery hens. They rear pets in odd corners—guinea pigs, hamsters, rabbits, mice, even snakes. I was fascinated to handle a gentle, full-grown python but wondered how he liked my warm sticky hands on his cool smooth skin. Jeremy, in his 'spare time', restores old motor cars, cuts up and retails firewood from their woodland thinnings, plants trees, mends fences and helps his parents attend to the many 'farm gate' sales (which always extend so far beyond the gate!) The telephone peals constantly and a hard day pony showing is a real day off for Brian and Betty now that Jeremy can hold the fort so well.

In the midst of all this busy-ness they took time off to welcome us: Betty cooked a wonderful meal— (meat and *four* veg.—imagine the trouble!) and afterwards we went round the ponies. Once, as we walked up a coppiced hillside, Betty and Mary returned to the house for a forgotten camera: I awaited them, sitting on my shooting stick among bird song in the warm autumn sunshine, and knew one of those rare moments of pure joy. Then we climbed on up the hill to be met on the skyline by a magnificent bunch of ponies, Toogood and Triad among them and all was very well. We returned happily to Halse and home to work again next day.

After we finished with visiting mares I had a near-breakdown: I needed to lie flat on my back at frequent intervals and felt the devastating depression which engulfs one when overtired. A few days ordered rest in bed and a patient search by our doctor for the right drug to replace my used-up chemicals soon improved me, but some depression remained: I seemed to have lost purpose in life. Then I fell deeply in love with a mind. There were frequent long stimulating telephone talks about books, people, politics: I walked on air. When I asked Mary if she resented all this she replied: 'I mind nothing so long as you are happy.' I was, but after a couple of years the affair ended in unhappiness. Mary never faltered and our love grew and grew.

Orthodox religion was no answer. We are both baptised and confirmed members of the Church of England and before I met Mary I had a period of ardent Anglo-Catholicism, due to the influence of a much loved friend; but church attendance and farming Sunday mornings do not go well together and anyway I found myself unable to say the Creed with honesty. Mary maintained basic church going while her mother was alive, as she did not want to give hurt; but Christmas mornings especially were a struggle to get through, with Mary off, helpers short and the winter stock feeding to do. We felt in a desperate rush and were nearly always a bit late for the family mid-day meal at Leintwardine. We feel the peace and hope of Christmas more now and Christmas Eve is a special joy in this beautiful place, with the King's College carols on the radio in the afternoon and the whole Ashley family singing carols for us in the evening dusk. We try to hear the Queen on Christmas morning and the feeling of Family persists.

In 1976 the Diocese of Hereford initiatied a study course: 'Rural Society and the Church', and discussion groups were formed throughout the county. We joined the Kingsland group and sat, mostly tongue tied, through much frank and often forthright talk of education, race, religion, sex and morality. We were not actually discussing homosexuality when Michael Thomas, the young vicar of Dilwyn who died soon afterwards, remarked that there is so much of male and female in each of us that balance is hard to fine: I shall remember always the compassion in his voice. Homosexuality is a fact of life: as a four year old said to her mother 'We be what we are born, aren't we?' It is also a hard fact which many people still do not accept.

I was asked one night, before the meeting began: 'What is your religion?' I parried the question, but much later on, during general discussion, I was able to blurt out my belief that God is Love, and in

The weathervane that's travelled with us

Reverence for Life; but I think to myself that I am a farmer, whose job is to breed and rear animals for ultimate killing and eating; yet they might not have life at all unless we helped and cared for them. We all have to die: perhaps it is the manner and not the fact of death for which we are responsible. Then there is hunting, shooting, fishing—the instinctive pursuits of man, some good some bad in all of them: I simply do not know.

We are both members of CND and spent a year collecting signatures for the nationwide petition for multilateral disarmament, organised in the early 1980's. We found it a tough, tiring job but achieved about fifteen hundred signatures without too much difficulty, as so many agreed with the multilateral approach. No bricks were hurled, though a roadman shouted at us; but the worst was when a friend accused us of making a 'dishonest list': she said that some old people we had asked did not know what they were signing. She carpeted me in some form and then removed her name from our list, transferring it to a London collection. We both felt crushed; but we had done a good job together and our confidence soon returned.

We thought much of the future: with the help of Pamela and Raymond, our doctors and our friends, we hope to finish our lives here or in hospital. We could not bear to sell our home nor face another move: we tried not to be shaken when the 'carpeting' friend told us that we should be 'a little frightened' of planning to remain in such an isolated spot. I am often more than a little frightened of many things but it is no help to be told that you should be so! We plan and save, and hope together to be able to take what comes.

XVIII
Winding Down

We parted with the ponies at the right time: we wonder often how we should have managed to carry hay and water to them in the fierce winter of 1981-82. The first snow fell on December 8th, before the hundred and thirty Cwmwhitton ewes had gone for the winter: we carried bales in bits to them in the orchard and were mobbed and the hay trampled, because we were so slow. Verney and Colin came as soon as they could: it was impossible to get the lorry up the Lane, so the sheep were driven down to be loaded in the village, by courtesy of our kind neighbour, John Rees.

Christmas 1981 was white, with ten degrees of frost and brilliant sunshine on Christmas Day. We wished the Ovendens, our doctors' family, could come up and ski down the glistening snow-clad slope of Pony Bank. The snow on the Lane had hardened and the Landrover took us safely to and from Brian and Helen's family gathering at Staunton-on-Wye.

Soon after Christmas a quick thaw came, with lots of rain and wind; we hoped that the worst of the winter was over; but on January 8th the second snow began and continued for days and days. The Lane became impassable, with bank high drifts. We struggled down the field to Hill Croft every night and morning to adjust the heating, digging ourselves through the gateways: we carried a shovel everywhere. Each morning we dug ourselves out of the house across the yard to Jane's loose-box, into the meal house, into the hens: the yard was criss-crossed in three narrow trodden pathways between walls of snow, along which the cats tripped delicately. Jane trotted and we plodded, carrying buckets of firewood or hen feed. The hens refused to come out of their house until we were able to clear a place to spread straw for their corn scratch. Their water froze continually—we carried out a hot kettle every hour or so. On January 14th our yard thermometer registered thirty degrees of frost and then the mercury disappeared. At Hill Farm everything froze, including the mains water and the central heating boiler, then outside in the tack room. We melted snow, thanked God for the Aga and our good sitting room fire, and carried drinking water up from Hill Croft: we managed to keep the cottage thawed by an incredibly extravagant use of electricity. This and the telephone held throughout and as a forlorn hope we rang Deacons about the boiler. No vehicle could get up the Lane but to our amazement Beresford and his mate, Billy Brookes, arrived on foot, carrying between them their heavy plumbers' kit. They hacked up the concrete outside our Lane door, thawed out the pipe and got the boiler going: we sealed the trench with straw bales. Never were cups of coffee given more gratefully, but they were not so nice made with dried milk. We were days without bread or liquid milk, but were never hungry as we keep a good store of food and Mary made bread. Lack of milk was more of a hardship as we, the cats and Jane drink so much; but as soon as a team of Lucton schoolboys dug a pathway up the bottom pitch of the Lane one of the masters, Bill Berisford, and a couple of boys came up to us carrying bottles. The school has gone now and we miss it, but are thankful for the strong young presence of the Ashley family at Hill Croft. We have made provision for our old age as far as possible but one cannot plan wholly against the weather. We were lucky to need neither doctor nor ambulance during that tough spell.

In the following year Mary noticed an increasing dryness of her mouth: she carried a beaker of water in her pocket (which was often flooded!) and sipped constantly. Such a persistent lack of saliva took her to the doctor, who diagnosed Sjögrens' Syndrome, a rare progressive disease which dries up mouth and eyes: the lack of saliva affects the digestion and disintegrates the teeth—Mary has had several spells in hospital for extractions. What else it does we don't know yet and Mary copes marvellously; but it lurks in our lives.

We set out to arrange the essential routine work so that one of us, in health, could manage it on her own. For nine months of the year the various bunches of Cwmwhitton stock must be seen daily: Jane gathers the sheep for counting but we do not take her through the cattle and there is often much walking round a big bunch to make a true count. We find it hard to pick out the black cattle against the dark hedges: (no doubt this is a reason for the broad white shoulder belt which was bred into the black Galloway cattle to make a separate breed, the Belted Galloway.) One pouring wet morning I spent ages counting and re-counting until I convinced myself that there really was one missing and set out to search. In the farthest corner of the field, under the wood, I found the heifer grazing a few yards away from her huge Charolais calf which she had dropped a bit early; he was stretched out flat, quite dead I thought; but as I turned away I noticed the hint of a breath. I set at him with the kiss of life and vigorous slapping massage and he began to breathe regularly; I tried to turn him over but he was too heavy and wet. The rain was relentless and very cold—he needed to be rubbed dry and have warm milk in him; but I had to leave him lying in the wet grass while I struggled what seemed miles back to the house to telephone. He was still alive when Verney and Colin came to fetch him and his bewildered mum, but he died later. It was a traumatic experience for me: the time I lost counting, the lack of strength, no Mary to take over massage till Cwmwhitton came for she was ill in bed. Verney and Colin were so nice about it and promised in future to have the down calvers home earlier; but it was a failure of old age which I minded very much. We have always said that when a job cannot be done properly it should be given up; but while we remain here the stock will be seen daily by someone: with Cwmwhitton behind us we shall do the best we can.

We have great pride in our present poultry management and hope to continue hen keeping to the end. We run twelve to fifteen laying birds who live round the back of the barn. They sleep in the old stubble house in which we slept when we lambed down the ground at Brook Farm: it is stationary now on its stout iron wheels, but has worn wonderfully well over all the years; large enough to contain perches, nest boxes and a raised dry mash trough with a suspended water bucket, it is deep littered with sawdust and the birds are warm and comfortable while shut in. They run out into a large pen with a strawed scratching area for corn feeding, and on through a further pop hole to the green grass of Marian's Orchard, where they graze, shelter and dust bath under the massive holly hedge. Their rations are a balanced layers' meal, fed warm and wet in the run first thing and dry ad lib in the house, plus a generous feed of wheat in the evening, scattered in the scratching straw. There is always a plentiful supply of clean water, four or five little troughs in the run and about eight halved car tyres dotted about in Marian's Orchard, a supply appreciated also by wild birds and little animals, such as hedgehogs and mice.

We collect eggs several times a day, to guard against breakages (and magpie thefts) though with oyster shell always available to the birds the shells are generally good, though they vary with age and breed. We try to clear old hens regularly and at last have a humane outlet for them. This has been a difficulty lately: we used to kill and eat them ourselves, but Mary can no longer pluck and draw, and my hand is not strong enough now for the swift neck dislocation which was also a knack. We are grateful that Ralph and Mary Owen will accept a few live two and three year olds when they come to pick up apples each autumn.

In November Brian and Betty French bring us half a dozen pullets of varying breeds and crosses: the difference in behaviour and performance is interesting, though all lay well for us. We have a small egg round in the village, which keeps us in touch with our friends, and our customers like the coffee coloured eggs of the black

Marans, which we find bad tempered bossy birds. One year we had pure bred Rhode Island Reds, richly red in colour, handsome and gentle, a beautiful and one-time common breed now classed as rare. We have only one Welsummer, a fine creature who lays well for us—we shall be sorry to see her go; but the R.I.R.-Light Sussex cross are not as good as they used to be. Last year came our first 'Warner' hybrids—enchanting creatures of gold and silver plumage who behave like little dogs, following and begging—they can be picked up readily. We suspect that Brian and Betty nurtured them specially for us this year: they are great fun and give us lots of pleasure.

The hen job is more than ever a life line now that Mary spends much time on her bed: the regular work takes me from the house and when Jane and I round the barn on our way to the pen we face first the wonder of the mountains and then turn to look upwards to Mary's window. The cheery wave and words of greeting send me on with a lift, or if she is asleep I can watch her and judge if she needs me soon. We are so lucky to be together and still able to communicate so well.

It was a frosty February morning in '87 when Mary returned from the early field round saying that she felt giddy and must go to bed; she thought she had the 'flu. She was in the course of a blood test initiated by the doctor who spotted an enormous bruise on Mary's thigh: 'Oh it's nothing—I bruise so easily'. Later in the morning the telephone rang: the blood test result had come and Mary might qualify for the Guinness Book of Records as she had only four blood platelets. (Platelets are one of the factors which promote blood clotting: the average in normal blood is two to three hundred.) She must go to hospital that afternoon for a transfusion. Mary pleaded to stay till next morning, and was allowed to do so provided that she promised not to move from her bed; but in the middle of the night she had an internal haemorrhage and vomited blood. I phoned the doctor, who was off duty I knew, and was met with an instant caring response: the ambulance from Hereford was at Hill Farm within forty minutes. The men were kind and gentle as they carried Mary

225

down our winding stairs; when they had settled her inside the driver turned to me and named the ward at the County Hospital and also the sister in charge ('She's a lovely person—she'll take care of you: ring at 7 in the morning and you'll see.') Then the wan figure inside raised an arm in salutation, the door closed and the ambulance slid down into the darkness of the Lane.

I was numb and slept four hours: at 7.10 a.m. I rang and a charming nurse assured me that Mary was 'comfortable' (she wasn't!) and in the middle of a blood transfusion: 'Come to see her whenever you like.' Kind friends drove me down as I could not face driving by myself in the Landrover when tired and stressed. I got an hour with Mary and was able to be near her bed when a bone marrow sample was taken: the news that it was negative came as a huge relief next day. The following week was like a bad dream, but I was supported magnificently by Pamela, who came each day, between her school work, to fix my food and square up in the house, while I did the outside work and got ready for the mid-day hospital spell. After forty-eight hours of continuous blood transfusion Mary looked a different person: she was wound up with steroids and I had a job to keep up with her cheerful chat! The doctors and nurses were marvellous and the ward became home from home; but after ten days we were utterly thankful to have her back home in bed, where she could see the mountains again. That was the night when I met David Ashley by the orchard gate.

A quiet time followed for Mary, with regular blood tests by our own doctors; but after a month she was whisked back to hospital for more transfusions, as the platelet count had fallen again to ten. She has a serious blood disorder and needs to attend regularly at hospital for blood tests and drug adjustments, though after two years the time gap has widened to two months. We feel at home in the Haematology Department, with the friendly faces of patients and staff: the large waiting room is also a passage where white coated figures hasten to and fro (is it the fashion for housemen to leave their coats unbuttoned?) and high heels click constantly—their wearers must be tired by the end of the day. There are huge tropical plants, convenient loos and a splendid aquarium of brilliant fish, a recent and fascinating gift. From the patients' point of view Haematology at the County is a very pleasant department.

Mary worked quietly on through the summer and autumn of 1987: she managed the mowing, though the ride-on mini-tractor shook her up a great deal—the 'lawn', after the water upheaval, is extremely uneven. Fortunately the cider apple crop was light: Mary did no picking up, because the stooping made her nose bleed, but Pamela did wonders, I did a little and Raymond loaded the Landrover in his dinner hour from Wigmore School. We have a large number of lightweight bags and with only two buckets full of apples in each, and Raymond's expert loading, we could get half a tonne on the Landrover and pull them off ourselves at Bulmers without strain: we were always directed to an easy channel and never hurried there.

We enjoyed our weekly journeys specially that year, with Mary so much better. After unloading we drove across to Bulmers' railway siding and ate our sandwiches near the old signal box which used to control the truck loads of French fruit coming in to the channels. We could watch the private steam engine at shunting practice, the birds on the embankment and the coming and going of luncheon guests to the smartly decorated dining car which stood permanently on the siding. Once we were challenged by stern security men in uniform; ('What are you doing here?') but they soon melted when we told them exactly what we had been doing, from entering the gate to the needed rest before driving out again into the traffic. Thereafter they greeted us with a grin and a wave.

When we reported to our friends in the fruit office our final load for '87 we guessed that it would be our last: we could manage no longer a heavy crop on our own and the cost and hassle of hired transport would be hopelessly uneconomic. When we received Bulmers' invitation to offer our fruit in 1988 Mary was laid low with shingles: it was with a heavy heart that I wrote 'None' across the reply card.

We wondered all summer how best to sell our fruit 'on the trees': to advertise would bring in far too many unknowns. Then Colin introduced us to Ralph and Mary Owen, who make their own cider and sell a few bottles, in various vintages, from their small farm near Kinnerton. They have a century old cider press, which they demonstrate at shows: it runs off an ancient David Brown tractor. One November morning they brought and set up in our orchard the tonweight press and we saw our own apples crushed on the spot: Ralph and his son James tended the machine, Mary and daughters Katherine and Christine picked up apples while Raymond and I looked on. Mary was too ill to come out but was able to watch from the window: it was a memorable experience and so kind of the Owen family to take such trouble.

The horrible shingles hit Mary in July '88. She thought at first that she had an insect bite on her temple, but it became worse and she went to the doctor for an antibiotic. He mentioned shingles and asked her to return next day, but by then she felt too ill to move, so he came to her—he visited her seven times during the first two weeks of her illness. The swift diagnosis and careful treatment saved her eye, already sore with Sjögrens, but the pain in ear and jaw was excruciating—she was exhausted after the spasms.

The sore on her temple suppurated for weeks and after ten months the ear is still giving great pain. She was beginning to get about a little when she developed 'flu and spent a week back in bed over Christmas. We missed the family gathering with Brian and Helen on Christmas Day, but the Ashley family ran up the Lane with a full Christmas dinner for us, wrapped in hot towels: it was wonderfully kind and bucked us up no end. Pamela as always was a tower of strength and brought us cooked food for weeks: each day we said together 'Anyway Mary is HERE, not in hospital'. She was able to look out on the mountains and the cheerful greetings from her bed spurred us on. Since then she has had dermatitis, itching madly all over, for the drug she must take for her blood condition makes her susceptible to every infection. But with the constant care of our

Off to feed the hens

Kingsland doctors she WILL get better from this wretched shingles—she makes a little progress every day. She is doing our cooking now and has taken over from me the mole tump job on the lawn. (We push creosoted corks down the hole in the centre of the tump; the mole hates them in his passage ways and in time retreats from the garden. We are amazed that otherwise humane people allow moles to die slowly in holding traps or be poisoned with strychnine.) On good days Mary walks the fields again and with heaven-sent health I can manage the outside routine. We will try to carry on here as well as may be for years yet.

Above all we must be able through their childhood to *Welcome The Workers!* In 1979 my niece Emma married Babar Khan Mumtaz, a Pakistani architect and development planner, and each year their children, our 'grandchildren', Chungaiz and Aruna have come to help us on the farm. We feed and water the hens together and they collect the eggs; we count the cattle, gather the sheep with Jane, check for sore eyes and lame feet, and talk mightily as we move from field to field. They help us change the litter in the hen house; they cut up firewood for our winter store. Last thing at night we shut the hens' pophole, stroke a hen or two, check the locks on the forest gates and go to bed happy. In the morning Mary and I talk of the day's work, past and to come.

cut up firewood for our winter store. Last thing at night we shut the hens, popphole, stroke a hen or two, check the locks on the forest gates and go to bed happy. In the morning Mary and I talk of the day's work, past and to come.

IXX
The Happy Farmers

Small children have called us *'The Happy Farmers'*. I think that few farmers can be entirely happy in their life of incessant struggle with weather, markets and disease; while few in old age can be happy with the aches and pains, the ills and accidents, the diminishing powers and (for me) the haunting fear of the future. But we are happy in our home, our friends and our love, so maybe we have earned that touching title.

Also from Logaston Press

Walks & More, by Andrew Johnson & Stephen Punter
Aspects of Herefordshire, by Andrew Johnson & Stephen Punter
Aspects of Worcestershire, by Andrew Johnson & Stephen Punter
Ludford Bridge and Mortimer's Cross, by Geoffrey Hodges
The Humble-bee Its Life History and How to Domesticate it, by F.W.L. Sladen